THE GOOD THINGS IN LIFE

THE GOOD THINGS IN LIFE:

A NURSE'S STORY OF CONNECTION

CHRISTOPHER KRAMER, RN

The Good Things In Life: A Nurse's Story of Connection
Copyright © 2020 by Christopher Kramer

Published by Cincinnati Book Publishing, Cincinnati, Ohio
www.cincybooks.com
Anthony W. Brunsman, president
Sue Ann Painter, executive editor
Alaina Stellwagen, assistant editor
Kayla Stellwagen, designer
Faith Scully, assistant editor

Cover Designer: Daniel M. Ruberg
Development Editor: Katie Holocher
Photographer: Jenn Mercer

ISBN   978-1-7349967-7-7

Author Contact Information:
Email: kra7mb@gmail.com
Facebook: www.facebook.com/chris.kramer.9674
Linkedin: www.linkedin.com/in/chris-kramer-rn-msn-79710531/
Author is available for book signings, speeches, and lectures by request.

Printed in the United States of America

First Edition, 2020

To my wife and children, the loves of my life.
To everyone who's searching—
Never give up.

Contents

Part 3: **Beyond**

Foreword

Connection. It's a powerful word. I'd put it up there with words like, "caring" or "empathy" or even "love." Mostly, because you can't have any of those awesome experiences without connection.

If there's any profession in the world that exemplifies "connection" it's nursing, and certainly all of healthcare for that matter. In that world, a world I know well as a nurse since 1993 and a world the author of this book knows well, connection can be the difference, literally, between life and death. With connection you build, you help, and you heal. I'm sure you'd agree we could use more builders, helpers, and healers in this world.

Chris and I share quite a bit in common, with Pediatric Nursing, a shared love, being the biggest connection we have. Being a pediatric nurse teaches you, very quickly, how important it is to authentically "connect." You can't fake connection when you're taking care of kids! They see "fake" from a mile away. Communication has to be honest, frequent, and from the heart. As I always say, you will treat and heal your patients more with the words you use than with any medication or treatment you can possibly dispense. Chris talks a lot about his experiences in his pediatric nursing life and I'm sure you will find, as I did, those stories are poignant and beautiful.

Chris Kramer's book is all about "connecting" and he speaks about it from his authentic life experiences—experiences many readers of this book will find familiar, real, and touching because they'll sound a lot like their own. See, that's how you can tell when you're reading a good book—when you can see yourself in it. As I read Chris's book, I saw myself in it.

You will too.

Chris talks about connection not from a purely academic standpoint but from one of real life. Maybe it's just me but these days, I quite enjoy things that are "real." Those are the things that make life, with all of its challenges and imperfections, beautiful.

Connection is beautiful.

Chris is a special guy. You will hear that in every word. This is a book about his journey. But after reading it, you may realize it's about yours as well.

–Rich Bluni, RN

Author of: *Inspired Nurse, Inspired Nurse Too!* and *Oh No! Not More of That Fluffy Stuff*

Prologue

Being human isn't easy or predictable but the experience sure can be beautiful. The possibilities associated with choice, the power of hope, the courage needed to self-reflect into change, and the ability to adapt have forced me to ask a tough question (many times): who am I?

I'm a registered nurse who works in pediatric health care. Honestly, had you asked the twelve-year-old version of me where I'd be in ten years, a hospital wouldn't have reached my top twenty guesses. My first answer then would've been associated with soccer or a zoo. It's funny how things change over the course of time.

I'm just going to be clear about something right away: I'm just an ordinary guy. I come from a middle-class family in Kentucky, and lived a childhood where I was able to grow with the right guidance. I was fortunate enough to have been loved by a family who cared about each other. My parents both came from strong German Catholic families where hard work wasn't just a value, but a way of life. My mom's father was a World War II veteran and made a living post-war running his own grocery store. My grandma was a stay-at-home mom who raised five children in a three-bedroom house. My dad's parents came to America from Germany in the 1930s. His father was a carpenter and his mother was also a stay-at-home mom. They bought a nice plot of land and, wouldn't you know it, raised five children in a three-bedroom house.

My parents carried that same work ethic and demeanor into their adult lives. My father took up the carpentry family business and my mother worked for 35 years at the IRS. While my dad was able to get a college degree, my mom managed to build a successful career with only a high school diploma. Both could not be better role models. They paid for my school, allowed me to play sports, and showed me that being a good person trumps all things. My family was important to me but I don't think I ever understood how lucky I truly was.

My grandparents have all since passed away but I was able to develop relationships with most of them well into my twenties, and my parents couldn't be more supportive, kind, and generous people. These early relationships built a foundation and are very special to me. Connections amongst people are unique and, for whatever reason, some people seem to form a bond easier and faster than others, even within a family. It's not easy to recognize lessons from these relationships, as quite often, we tend to take them for granted. I'm no different because to this day it still takes me time to see the importance of connection, at all levels.

For as long as I can remember, I've felt a strong urge to matter. It's an urge that was never based on personal accomplishment or wealth, but more a sense of wanting to leave this world a better place than when I entered it. That urge drove me to try and excel at anything and everything. Throughout my early school years, I wanted to play sports, be a part of student government, make good grades, perform in school plays, and be popular. I had this idea that success was associated with making a difference. If I could succeed, I would be recognized, and if I were recognized, I would matter. So I always tried to succeed and left little room for failure. If something wasn't good enough, I was the first one in line to take the job of "toughest critic." This resonated into college as I joined a fraternity and constantly felt self-imposed pressure to excel. Along this journey, I failed many times, made some bad choices, and learned how to live out of the protective home I'd grown accustomed too. However, during this time, my life's passion would unveil itself in a form that certainly brought me a significant amount of surprise.

I discovered nursing. Through that discovery, I was shown a path of making a difference that wasn't measured by success but rather by connection—connection with people at the most intimate level. This revelation was life-altering as it had me evaluating the very definition of who I was. It had me wondering what kind of person I wanted to be and what kind of legacy I wanted to leave. I wanted to learn about people and I wanted to connect with them.

This type of discovery came with a great deal of self-reflection. I had been so focused on success that I hadn't really evaluated the relationships in my own life (like the ones mentioned earlier) and just how much I had learned from them. The knowledge I gained from those connections began to enhance not only the career path I chose, but also to shape my lifelong values. My journey navigating the value of human connection brings stories of relationships both old and new. And it starts at an early age.

When I was a senior in high school I went on a Christian Awakening Retreat. Prior to the weekend, each participant's friends and family members were asked to write letters. If they chose to do so, the letters were given to the participants in an envelope midway through the retreat. There was one letter, in particular, that I vividly remember reading from my grandpa. It wasn't fancy or long, in fact, it wasn't even on stationary paper. It was the only letter that was in a greeting card and it said one thing:

"May you only have the good things in life."

At the time I thought he was talking about not experiencing anything bad in life. However, I've come to realize that he wasn't referring to tragedy, but was rather hoping that I'd discover the things that truly mattered.

Connections like that gave my life perspective and purpose, hope for the future, and continually revealed new things to me. There is no discrimination and there are no rules. There's only an overarching question: how will the experiences and people in your life today affect the person you'll be tomorrow?

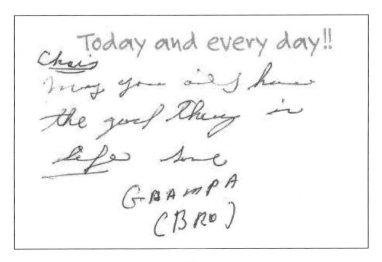

Part 1

GROWTH

Chapter 1

Is Connection Rare?

I remember my first clinical experience in nursing school. It was at a nursing home. The night before, I was assigned the task of creating care plans for two to three patients. I was to come in the next day and care for them in adjunct with the staff nurse. Walking into my first patient's (a complete stranger) room at 7:00 a.m. was an uncomfortable situation. I wasn't really sure what to say (or if I should even speak), how I should say it, what information I should give, or the way in which I should give it. I don't remember much about the interaction, but I do remember being uncomfortable, feeling very shy, and starting the conversation with a, "Hi, uhhhh...." (Articulation at its best).

Have you ever heard that you may only really connect with one or two people in your lifetime? Or heard about how rare a true mental connection with someone is? I disagree.

I think that there's real opportunity to connect with anyone I meet for the first time. There's an opportunity to break down walls, eliminate barriers, understand their perspective, listen to what they have to say, and converse about differing/alike opinions. This is, potentially, something that can occur daily and something that can enrich life. It's not spontaneous and takes a certain level of self-awareness coupled with, in my experience, two additional components: effort and communication.

By definition, effort is strenuous physical or mental exertion. The experience of effort could be described as the particular feeling of that energy being exerted and is accompanied by a sensation of strain and labor, a feeling that intensifies the harder a person tries. Essentially, perception of effort is a cognitive feeling of work associated with voluntary actions, and is crucial for the judgment of personal actions.

After my initial patient encounter blunder, I eventually became more and more comfortable with bedside nursing situations as I cared for more and more patients, but it was a process. Through that process I started to figure out that I could be as warm, personable, and caring as I wanted to be (personal controllable action). The more I was involved, the more the patient opened up and was comfortable with me; the less personable I was, the less the patient wanted to be cared for by a student/new nurse/stranger. There was a clear, direct relationship and it was apparent that my effort was of prime importance. My perception of that effort made a huge difference; feeling like I was trying hard for a desired outcome was far more effective than feeling like I hardly had to try at all for the same desired outcome.

Strong effort and perception of that effort in building meaningful emotional connections reminded me of another passion of mine: endurance sport. In a way I could correlate this to training for a race. The more miles I put in, the easier the workouts felt, consequently reducing the amount of effort I eventually needed to execute (trying hard versus hardly trying for the same result). Practice, repetition, and time in putting forth effort ultimately would teach me how difficult or easy it would be to connect with someone.

Effort was once thought to be involved in the regulation of human behavior. This was eventually confirmed by something called the motivational intensity theory. In essence, are you motivated to approach a specific situation or remove yourself from it? In the context of endurance and exercise (where effort and perception of effort have been studied most), the psychobiological model suggests that athletes will engage in exercise until the maximum amount of effort they are willing to exert (i.e. potential motivation) is reached. In that context, the psychobiological model suggests that athletes will adjust the intensity of the exercise when they reach maximum amount of effort they are willing to exert, or when success seems impossible.

Could the meaningfulness of an interaction between two people be partly defined in a similar way? When meeting someone for the first time I'm actively choosing to exert or not exert mental and emotional energy that intensifies the harder I try. At this point one of two things can happen: that effort is reciprocated, building the connection, or the maximum effort I was willing to put forth is reached, dissipating the interaction when success seems impossible.

Regardless of those two outcomes my engagement is required, and without it, a connection is always impossible.

In discovering the role of effort in my day-to-day interactions, I came to realize that living my life with an open heart and mind, not guarded by walls, completely changed my perception. My actions needed to be positively conditioned toward the needs of others. Effort by itself, however, isn't powerful enough to stand on its own. Effective communication is also required to complete the connection equation.

When it comes to building a connection, effort is wasted if communication is absent. Effort must be channeled, yes, but it also must be delivered effectively. In my bedside experience, patients and families need to know that I am putting forth the effort to heal their child, and that can be apparent through action, but it's also highly dependent on communication. My "Hi, uh...." blunder wasn't a very good first impression nor was it effective communication.

When I walk into a room for the first time to take care of a patient, those first few minutes are incredibly important. Think about the scenario for a second. The parents (no matter how long they've been there) are exhausted, scared, and in an unfamiliar environment. Likewise, and probably amplified, for the patient. How would you feel if I walked into your child's hospital room, said nothing, and just started tinkering with things? Skeptical? Distrusting? Upset? All the above?

This isn't specific to any profession. Being a good communicator takes open-mindedness and active listening—things that can be practiced every day. I've never successfully interacted with someone while angry about their perspective or while just waiting for my turn to speak (even though I've been guilty of doing both of those things, more than once). It's a learning process, a journey; a chance to fail, learn, and adapt.

Communication, be it effective or ineffective, is something that has been dissected a lot over the years. In a recent study performed by nursing educators it was shown that the two most important points were "approach" and "aspects of nonverbal communication." The "approach" piece is concerned with rapport-building and other behaviors associated with a positive "manner" towards others. It entails developing strategies for engagement and relationship building. How someone is approached sets the stage; it prepares both individuals for either a successful or unsuccessful interaction.

Feedback in this study, which specifically focused on non-verbal communication, highlights the importance of direct eye contact as well. I don't know why it's so difficult but I find myself looking away from people while speaking, all the time. I have to actively focus on remembering to look people in the eyes. Being aware is half the battle because once I made it a priority I now can't converse with someone without reminding myself to constantly look him or her in the eye. I believe in eye contact; it shows people I'm focused on them and what they have to say. It shows I care.

Figure out what deficits you have to being a good communicator. Are they inhibiting your ability to connect with others in a really meaningful way?

In 2014, after I obtained a master's degree in nursing, I accepted a new position that took me away from direct bedside care. It was a difficult decision as I love taking care of patients, but it has involved me in many other important aspects of health care. The importance of connection hasn't fallen to the wayside, however, as I have to utilize the skills I learned while directly interacting with patients, just in a different manner. I can't really explain this concept so philosophically without providing real life context. Therefore, I'm going to go back and navigate through a much more thorough journey that highlights just how much there is to learn about human connection. I'm going to start from the beginning.

Chapter 2

Be Honest

My dad has always been, and forever will be, a truck lover. He's always had one. I think mainly because he needs it for his contracting work, but also because his dad always had one too. It was a common bond they shared together and I believe when he rides in his truck he feels closer to his dad; their connection amplifies as he sits in that driver seat. I think it brings him back to the little boy he was sitting there as a passenger. Sitting there in admiration, soaking up knowledge, and learning everything he could from the man controlling the wheel. Always wondering, in excitement, where they would go next.

Twenty years ago, I was the little boy sitting in the truck staring at my dad. I didn't follow in the same footsteps as he did, since I can barely swing a hammer much less build a house or remodel a room; that gene seemed to bypass my DNA makeup. Nonetheless, I admired the man driving that truck, teaching me things much more important than just how to work with tools.

There's a particular day all those years ago that stands out as a little different. It was right after my grandpa passed away and my dad was a little more silent than usual, a little sadder. I didn't get to know my grandpa very well, as I was still pretty young when he died, but I knew him to be a good man and knew he meant a lot to my dad.

I remember breaking the silence with a pretty simple question:

"Dad, what do you think people will remember most about Grandpa?"

It's funny the things you remember while other things you can't remember at all. I remember exactly where we were driving when I asked this, I remember which season it was, and what the weather was like outside. I think things that really mean something to you tend to stick, and my dad's answer struck me differently that day because it wasn't at all what I expected.

I thought he'd say something about hard work, about how he made his own way in America, or maybe the fact that he used to pour oil on driveway weeds to kill them. Rather, he said,

"Probably that your grandpa was the most honest man they'd ever met."

I further inquired about what that meant and he explained how he, both in his personal life as well as professional, not only did great work but was also always fair, respectful, and told the truth. My dad, furthermore, modeled that behavior as well. This really resonated with me in a powerful way as two of the most influential male figures in my life connected on a common ideal. An ideal that was worth carrying on, worth implementing, and worth amplifying. This got me wondering, is being honest more than just the act of telling the truth? I used to think that's all it was.

The more I reflected on it, the more I realized how much more it was. Every once in a while I'll read something that really affects me. It doesn't happen often, but when it does, I change just a little bit. Many years ago I read *The Shack*, a Christian novel by William Paul Young. One short sentence from that book transported me to that moment in the truck with my dad. It read:

"Always take the risk of honesty."

Embedded within that sentence is much more than just an act of telling the truth or deciding not to tell a lie. It highlights a way of life. Through strong fatherly connections, this way of life was presented to me at a young age and has been reaffirmed as an adult time and time again. When you decide to be honest, you're committing to tell the truth, yes, but you're also building character, showing integrity, and proving that the temporary veil of a lie isn't as important as doing what's right. It shows that when facing adversity, no matter what, being a good person is always worth the risk.

Chapter 3

Reach Out

Growing up, I thought my parents had the perfect marriage. They never seemed to fight, my brother David and I always had everything we needed, and we spent an ample amount of time together as a family. Then one warm summer morning when I was 11 years old, my parents decided to blindside us with a family meeting.

"We've decided to separate," they said.

I don't remember much about the conversation but do remember feeling confused with the explanation and crying uncontrollably. Unbeknownst to me at the time, "separation" didn't mean divorce, but it was a necessary step married couples have to take before getting divorced. Most of this timeframe was a blur but during this separation me, at 11, and David, at 17, were allowed to reside in our childhood home. My parents, on the other hand, had to trade off weeks staying with us. The weeks they weren't at the house they would stay at a rented apartment. It was weird visiting them on their off weeks in an apartment. It felt foreign, wrong, and against the natural order of things in my life.

They divorced when I was twelve. I know the marriage divorce ratio statistic is not good and if I had to guess, I'd say the separation to divorce ratio statistic is even worse. They called another family meeting, and this time it was a little different. I was still confused by a weak explanation, but I didn't cry. I guess I knew what was coming.

"We took each other for granted," they said.

Now, I can't imagine what this was like for my parents, nor is it something I want to understand as a happily married adult now. However, from my perspective, it was the most challenging thing I had been through, and to this day is still one of the hardest life-altering events I've had to endure.

Luckily, I didn't have to go to court or pick which parent I wanted to live with as they agreed on 50/50 joint custody. This did mean, though, that I would have to move houses every Sunday for the unforeseeable future. Since David was 18 at the time and moving to college, this also meant that they'd have to drop me off every week. With all that, I'd never felt more alone, confused, and broken. For six years I felt like I was constantly on the move with no true home. Holidays were split, birthdays were no longer shared, and the guilt that came with doing something with one parent and not the other still haunts any family decision I now have to make.

David and I dealt with this split very differently. I turned to friendships that have since turned into lifelong bonds, while he was able to use college as a way to distance himself from it. At the time we weren't close; we had lived by the whole "I love you because I have to" concept. I had always looked up to him and wanted to be around him, though. I used to follow him and his friends around as best I could. They'd play roller hockey, see me hanging around, and make me be the goalie because I was the only one who was "good" at it. I'd then get pelted with tennis balls for the next hour. I didn't care though; I was part of the game. He also would use the upstairs facilities to go "number two" then call my name, and because I was young and stupid, I'd go, only to have him hold me in there with his hand over my mouth so that I'd have smell his terror. Funny, sure, but also disgusting. We had never been on the same page, especially given our age difference, but things were different now.

This split sparked a commonality and connection between us that hadn't existed before. I knew he was concerned about me because as time went on, I'd receive more and more calls and check-ins from him. As I got older, that one commonality grew into several, and as a senior in high school, I distinctly remember the moment I saw him as more than a brother I "have to love."

I played high school soccer and was going into my final senior season. It was the end of two-a-days, the team had been selected, and I was going to be a starting midfielder. David had just graduated from college and had accepted a job in Columbus, Ohio. One day I received a letter from him, which was right before my first game. The contents weren't anything fancy or long, but they didn't have to be. He wrote about how much he admired my dedication and hard work. He wanted to wish me luck on the upcoming season and told me to not take anything for granted. I remember this so vividly because he was more than just my brother now— he was a friend who cared about me. That letter took effort and showed appreciation for a bond that had significantly grown.

The connection that David and I share has been so important to me and keeps growing. It stemmed from something very difficult for both of us. Something that brought us together in a way I'm not sure anything else would have. There truly is good that comes out of bad situations. You may not want to see it or it may take a long time, but if you look, then look closer, something great may reveal itself. I'm grateful for the brother I have and the connection we continue to learn from. It's shown me that if a glass is half full that means there's extra room to fill it back up to the top; room enough to develop something that wasn't there before. Take advantage.

Chapter 4

Dream

Deciding where I wanted to go to college was a tough decision for me. I went to Covington Catholic High School (an all-male Catholic school) and graduated with 114 guys. About 75% of the class went to either the University of Kentucky, the University of Louisville, or Northern Kentucky University. The other 25% were split among a variety of other schools. I wanted to deviate from the norm and create a different experience for myself.

For a long time, I was convinced that I was going to go Coastal Carolina University. I was fascinated with marine biology and could get in-state tuition there for majoring in Marine Science. *Finding Nemo* was also extraordinarily popular at the time and happened to be my favorite movie. It just made sense.

During the summer before my senior year, I went on a trip to visit the school and loved it. Consequently, I applied, got accepted, and had all signs pointing to a southern move come the following year. My parents however, being the wise old souls that they are, suggested I explore other places as well. After all, why not have a backup just in case something happened, right?

The only other school within the budget that I had any interest in was Western Kentucky University. It was three hours away (drivable but just far enough) and wasn't littered with people from the past four years. One Saturday my dad and I took a little road trip to visit. We signed up to go through a sort of "college fair." There would be time to explore the campus, walk around to speak with different school departments, a lunch, and a football game. I remember being completely closed off on the drive down. I was 17 years old, a senior, had a new girlfriend, and in my mind was already down at Coastal. This whole thing was just a formality, something I was doing to satisfy my parents.

We arrived and started exploring the campus. It was beautiful. I was impressed right away, but wasn't going to tell my dad that as it wasn't quite enough to sway my decision (que bad attitude). The first stop was a walk around with the school departments in E.A. Diddle Arena to shop potential majors. We're sitting in this newly renovated building about to make our rounds (I'm still closed off) when my dad asked me this question:

"Have you ever considered becoming a nurse?"

It was like someone punched me in the face while screaming because I woke up immediately.

Up until that moment, the thought had never once crossed my mind. However, inexplicably, nothing had ever made more sense to me so quickly. All of my thoughts about Coastal, moving south, and the fascination with marine science seemed to dissipate in an instant. I can't really explain why. There are few moments in life where things are just clear, they make sense, and for lack of any better reason, you just know what you're supposed to do. That question sparked something within me that hadn't been there before.

I immediately thought of two things I knew up until this point in my life. One, I loved learning about the human body, having taken an Anatomy and Physiology class my junior year. Two, I wanted to matter. I wanted to make a difference.

I couldn't get to the WKU School of Nursing booth fast enough. I picked up a pamphlet and began my exploration of nursing. To this day, my dad and I continue to talk about that moment. He's still shocked at how much impact that question had on me because, on the outside, my attitude about the whole visit was so poor. However, what he didn't know was the reason behind my flat affect in the second half of the visit. I was excited about the revelation to venture down a path I hadn't thought of before. I was also conflicted about the decision I now had to make.

This part of my life is cluttered with inner struggle. I felt that nursing was my true path but the appeal of moving to South Carolina and doing something completely different was extremely enticing. My parents didn't understand. Ultimately, I did lots of my own research in both areas behind the scenes. Sometimes you just have to figure things out for yourself. You have to come to the answer organically rather than have someone else show it to you. This culminated into a final decision at the eleventh hour.

I was sitting in my third period study hall six months after that college visit to WKU. I still had not made a final decision. My parents thought I was all in on Coastal, though. I knew I was on the clock and time was running out. For no real reason at all, I was suddenly struck with a profound feeling of the path I needed to take and the choice that needed to be made. I excused myself and ran to the school office to call my dad. He answered and I frantically asked,

"Did you cancel my acceptance to WKU yet?"

He replied, "No, I was going to do that today. Why?"

"Don't, that's where I want to go next year, cancel Coastal."

I was a Hilltopper the next year as a pre-nursing major.

I never thought that this would be the path my life would take, but then again, how often do things work out exactly the way you planned? Sometimes it turns out better. Looking back on it now, I realize that the attributes I acquired through my family relationships (honesty, always trying to be a good person, always trying to see the good out of bad situations) completely directed this major life decision. I didn't see it at the time but this path chose me, not the other way around.

Inner-connection and self-discovery are major parts of growing up—finding yourself and the passion in your life. Passion can direct you to places that otherwise might be too scary to go. It will make you feel uncomfortable and probably create goals that seem unattainable, but there is nothing more worth doing. Find the passion in your life and don't stop until you've achieved everything you've wanted to achieve. After all, if you never try you'll never know, and not knowing is worse than trying and failing.

Chapter 5

Stay Engaged

I don't know how other people felt about making the transition from high school to college academically, but for me, it was a little overwhelming. At eighteen years old and only having sat in classes 15-30 people deep my whole life, I was shocked to walk into a biology class of 100+ my first semester. The amount of autonomy given to the students for required reading/studying was unlike anything I'd experienced. I felt relatively well equipped from a knowledge standpoint, as I was fortunate to have a great high school educational base. However, I was used to more structure and accountability. There were more consequences for homework incompletions and remediation's for poor grades. There were also much more fruitful teacher-student relationships.

I had some awesome high school teachers but two (I'll call them Mr. H and Ms. B) in particular made an impact on me that has lasted well into adulthood. They took an interest in my development as a human, not just my grades. Mr. H built a connection with me through spirituality, asking difficult philosophical questions that most teachers would shy away from at that age. He's a big reason I'm a spiritual person and continue focusing on that aspect of my life. All because he took the extra effort. Ms. B opened my eyes to creativity. I was a big science guy up to this point and hadn't really tapped into my creative psyche. She's the reason I love to read and write, as well as the reason I see value in practicing those skills. Her ability to effectively communicate and teach was beautiful. So far in college, granted it was early on, I was yet to see the capacity to create those types of relationships. That opportunity seemed to be absent, much to my dismay, but life always has a tendency to surprise, especially when you least suspect it.

I had to complete a whole list of prerequisite nursing courses (with the necessary GPA) during my first two years in order to be eligible for the nursing school application process. Classes ranging from Spanish, to philosophy, to history, to science, with a variety of different class sizes and a variety of different expectations. It wasn't until my first Anatomy and Physiology course that I really started to enjoy academia at the collegiate level.

I was sitting in an extraordinarily basic classroom within the biological sciences building, and when I say basic, I mean a chalkboard, wooden desks, and a podium. I didn't understand why the class was so small compared to all the other classes, but it was a little reassuring since it was what I had been used to growing up. Most of the other students in the class were either pre-med or pre-nursing. I soon found out why there were so few people: A&P was the first real medical pre-requisite class people had to take before getting deeper into the curriculum. The average grade was a 'C' and the "change major" rate post-course completion was high. It was a weed out course.

The teacher walks in and has nothing on him. No briefcase, no papers/notes, no computer. He introduces himself.

"Hello everyone, I'm Dr. Mason, welcome to Anatomy I. Go ahead and open your books to page 1 and we'll get started."

Everyone looked at each other a little confused because the guy didn't even have a book. He picked up a piece of chalk and started lecturing. As he went along, I began to realize that everything he was explaining reflected what was in the book. He knew it all by heart.

Dr. Mason had a major impact on me. His class met three times per week for one hour and every day he'd walk in with nothing and say:

"Welcome back everyone, where'd we leave off last time?"

Someone would look at their notes, tell him, and he'd continue the lecture. He had this innate talent of being able to explain complex physiological processes, to the minute cellular level, and have it make sense to people. The content wasn't easy even though he made it seem like it. His teaching style connected with me and constantly had me craving to learn more. He always made himself available after class if you didn't understand something and his office door was always open. He knew everyone by name and actively took an interest in giving his students the best chance to succeed. He saw great potential in everyone and wanted to help. It may have been a weed out course but it wasn't because the teacher tried to make it difficult, quite the contrary.

I absolutely loved learning about the human body. Its capability, the physiologic complexity yet simple nature of its makeup, and its incredible resilience continue to astound me. If I felt drawn to the nursing profession before college, Dr. Mason was responsible for converting my passion into a reality.

Helping people realize their own potential is the backbone of one of life's greatest human connections: teachers and students. The modern world needs great teachers. Teachers who not only give students the opportunity to learn but also connect with them on a level that reveals the potential success they can have through education. Dr. Mason showed me this. He invested his time, energy, and career in helping young adults recognize their potential. It's something that can set the tone for someone's life. Something that can quite honestly save someone's life. I've been blessed to have some great teachers. Teachers who saw potential in me and made the effort to help me realize it.

Assess the connections you have with the great teachers in your life. Learn from them, challenge them, ask questions, and value that interaction.

Chapter 6

Don't Quit

At the start of every single semester in college I'd have a "freak out" moment. New classes, new teachers, overwhelming syllabi, and an abundance of new material. I'd always ponder:

"What did I get myself into; how am I going to do this?"

And every single semester my mom would have to talk me down and calm my anxiety. She was my safety net, my voice of reason, and my rock. I always imagined her sitting by the phone each afternoon in late August and January expecting my call of panic because every time I called, she was there. Once I accomplished my first college goal and was accepted into nursing school, that anxiety and panic only amplified.

My first semester of nursing school was brutal. The amount of homework, studying, and time dedicated to school increased tenfold. Furthermore, we had very minimal clinical experience exposure, which is what I was most looking forward to, actually interacting with patients. Our first and only clinical that semester was eight weeks in a nursing home.

When I first discovered that we were finally starting an actual clinical experience, I was so excited I immediately went out and purchased all the super sweet nursing school necessities: stethoscope, sphygmomanometer, clipboard, white scrubs, white shoes (Velcro kicks from Walmart), and lab coat (with the nursing patch ironed on). The first day approached when we had a tour scheduled and would meet the leadership group in charge of the home. My first mistake was wearing blue striped boxers underneath my white scrubs, clueing everyone into my underwear choice. My second mistake was having high expectations.

Nursing homes are necessary and there are a lot of good ones out there. I also understand the logic behind choosing that as a first clinical experience; it's a good place to learn basic nursing care with low patient acuity. However, nursing homes are extremely depressing, often times dirty, and offer very little in terms of echoing a nursing student's excitement to become a nurse.

I remember one of the first patients I ever took care of as a nursing student. We were learning how to give intramuscular injections and I was about to administer a pneumococcal vaccine. The patient was female and suffering from severe dementia. It was sad and eye opening at the same time, as I had multiple living grandparents at the time. She didn't know who we were, where we came from, and basically didn't know up from down. She was so emaciated that I could touch my thumb to my forefinger when grabbing her upper arm. When I finished prepping with an alcohol swab and stuck the needle into her "muscle," it was so atrophied that it actually went through and pricked her bone. Yes, her bone. She had no reaction. I, on the other hand, was horrified. I immediately pulled the needle back out and looked to my nursing mentor for guidance. I didn't want to give the injection but also had no idea what to do next. It was a rather helpless feeling. My teacher ultimately took over and finished the task.

That was not a good day for me; in fact, the whole first clinical experience really had me down. So much so that I wanted to quit. What did I do?

"Hey Mom, it's me, I want to quit...."

I went back to my rock and spent hours on the phone talking about it. She convinced me that I needed to, at least, give it one more semester. Complete one full year and give this thing a real chance.

"Don't do something like quit because you're afraid or because it's too hard," she'd say.

Quitting is an interesting concept in the modern landscape. Some people say that life is too short to do something you don't enjoy (which I believe to be true), while others stand firm that quitting is never an option. After much trial and tribulation, I've come to believe in not giving up: if you start something you should see it through until the end. This has taken me a long time to grasp, though. I've wanted to quit plenty of times in my life, plenty of times, and almost have on many of those occasions, but I've never once regretted sticking with something. You have to give yourself enough time to really determine what it is you're doing. All too often we react quickly to change; we decide that something is too hard based on a small sample size and we quit. Change is scary, change is different, and it is human nature to fear things that are different. Some of the greatest things that have ever happened to me started out as terrifying.

In this case, I came very close to letting that fear win, but one semester just wasn't enough time; my mom was right and our bond kept me going. So I went back for my spring semester and kept grinding. The work was still difficult and the material abundant, but more and different clinical experiences were beginning to escalate and that began to reinvigorate me. Little did I know that the time I would spend in a mental health ward would start me on the journey of discovering my passion and purpose.

Chapter 7

Open Up

One of the first classes I took my second semester in nursing school was Mental Health. The clinical experience that coupled with this class had us assigned to work in a psychiatric unit at a small community hospital.

I was on the evening shift (3 p.m. until 11 p.m.) and would care for one mentally ill patient per clinical day (the patient you study and care for changes every day). This duty came with some prep work, requiring me to come in early, access the chart of the patient I was assigned to, and study things like medical history, medication use, demographics, etc. During this experience, the registered nurse who actually worked on the unit and was mentoring/precepting me, would supervise while distributing medications but otherwise would allow me to interact with the patient freely.

The first patient I was assigned to was a middle-aged woman with severe depression. She had been in and out of this unit multiple times. I was a little nervous as I'd never been in this type of work before, and mental health is very different than other medical-surgical units. In other units, you treat acute or chronic physical illnesses that hopefully are cured via time, medicine, or surgery. Mental illness is a whole different animal. It requires interaction, sensitivity, and extensive empathy. I wasn't at all sure if I would be up to the task.

When I arrived to the unit and met her for the first time I had no idea what to expect. I had never (at least to my knowledge) really known anyone officially diagnosed with severe depression. Our first interaction was pleasant. She was a perfectly nice woman and was pretty receptive to having a student nurse with her, which can be hit or miss when going through clinical work. Initial feeling had all things pointing towards a very positive clinical day.

Now there are things you learn by reading "medical history" and other things you can only learn through true interaction. I don't know whether I missed it in her chart or not but I soon learned the root of her depression. A couple years back, she had lost her 18-year-old daughter in a car accident. She couldn't understand how this could happen, and now she couldn't find a purpose in life. She was understandably distraught; she blamed herself, she blamed God.

If you've never been in a psychiatric treatment unit before, it can be eye opening. The patient's room is as plain as it gets, with no amenities of any kind. This is done in order to reduce possible suicidal behavior. Furthermore, a patient's treatment consists of medication, meal times, and focus groups (repeat). The focus groups are somewhat similar to what you might see in a movie: patients and provider hovered in a circle telling stories and discussing feelings. I went to a couple of these with my patient that day where she remained very quiet. She was much more open with me in a one-on-one setting than in a group. Not at all surprising from a person suffering from this type of mental illness, but there was something else here; she never smiled.

We got about four hours into the shift that day and pretty much all I had done thus far was listen. My mind kept racing through possible things to say, protocols and scenarios from classes, and books on how to deal with this type of thing, but none of it seemed to apply or work.

Then it hit me: I don't have to cure her, and she's not looking for another clinician to give the same therapy that she's been receiving. She simply needed a friend. That suddenly became my goal: to connect with her as a person, not as a nurse, and more tangibly, to make her smile.

I went through the rest of the evening with the mindset of just being myself and forgot about trying to be a healthcare professional. I tried to bring more personality into it, tried treating her like I would treat a personal friend or family member, and I let myself be more vulnerable to really connecting with who she is. It wasn't easy to do as she was still a complete stranger to me, but on the other hand, it was worth a try. As I continued to do this, I continued to rethink my approach. The conversation was much more fruitful and engaging, but I couldn't seem to make her smile.

Control. People love having it, hate losing it, and somehow have obtained all sorts of delusion surrounding what it means. I'm certainly guilty of letting things out of my realm of control affect my emotional state. It's an easy thing to let happen especially since there are all kinds of bad shit happening in this world, things that you may or may not have any influence over. Something horrific happened to this woman, something she had absolutely no control over, and she just couldn't see past it. There is no shame in this or judgment to be had; I mean, it's her daughter, who wouldn't be a complete mess? A smile is a powerful thing, though, and is always within our realm of choice and control. Sometimes it's all you need when looking for a glimpse of hope; after all, it's a scientific fact that smiling can have a positive effect on your mood. She deserved this choice in a time that probably seemed like all choice had been stripped from her.

Before I knew it, it was the end of the night and time for me to leave. We were chatting in her room—she resting on the bed and I was sitting on the floor— when my clinical instructor knocked on the door to wrap things up. We were in the middle of a pretty engrossing conversation where she was pouring her heart out about not wanting to live without her daughter. Sympathetically, I remember standing up to a final thought rushing into my mind. I walked over to her bedside, grabbed her hand, and said,

"I really enjoyed today and truly can't imagine having to go through what you've had to go through. I know I'm young, I'm inexperienced, and you have no reason to listen to me, but there are three things I've come to know in my short life: there is a God, I'm not Him, and to never give up no matter what happens. I hope you find what you're looking for."

With that, she said thank you and smiled.

Chapter 8

You Have a Purpose

Western Kentucky University is about an hour north of Nashville, and henceforth, Vanderbilt University. My first semester senior year, all of the nursing students took a field trip down to Vanderbilt Children's Hospital. Up until that point, I hadn't given much thought into what kind of nurse I wanted to be. I hadn't started applying for any jobs yet, nor had I really even thought about the process. At 21 years old, I was, to be completely honest, a little terrified to make the decision. I mean, how was I supposed to know something as important as which career path I should take? Wasn't choosing the nursing profession enough? The rest should just work itself out, right? Unfortunately, that's just not how things work.

The pediatric class I took one semester prior was only half a semester (the other half was obstetrics) and there wasn't a children's hospital in Bowling Green, so the clinical experiences were weak. Needless to say, my clinical exposure to pediatrics was minimal.

When I got off of the bus at Vanderbilt and took my first steps into the welcome area foyer, I was mesmerized. It was open, warm, inviting, and playful. I'm not sure I've ever truly grown up, so seeing the colorful decorations and an environment specifically tailored to healing children directly spoke to me. It was magical. My heart was racing with excitement during the entire visit and, for the first time, made me think about focusing on pediatric nursing.

I was restless the entire way home and couldn't wait to start researching my next moves. I was sitting next to one of my best friends (we pretty much got each other through nursing school), and he noticed my frazzled state.

"Dude, what the hell is wrong with you?"

"I know what I want to do now when we graduate. That place totally convinced me on pediatrics. I'm too excited to sit still and need to figure out where I should go."

Knowing the area I'm from he replied,

"You do know that there's a children's hospital like ten minutes from where you grew up and is an incredibly well-known pediatric institution, right?

I was embarrassed. I had no idea that was there; just goes to show how sheltered and ignorant I was at the time. When I got back to school, I immediately started looking at the hospital and what I could do there. I was attracted to a critical care nursing position they had available. I applied, was interviewed, and was offered a position over the next few months. Consequently, by January and the start of my last semester in college, I had accepted the offer to be a bedside Registered Nurse in the pediatric intensive care unit (PICU). This would become my first real job in healthcare.

Deciding to work with children turned out to be one of the easiest decisions of my life. Children are such an innocent and resilient population. They're more fun, they complain a hell of a lot less than adults, and the physical/mental strength of their bodies is the most scientifically marvelous thing I've witnessed. All children deserve the opportunity to live a safe and healthy life. They all have the right to grow up with every available advantage and need people that can help provide this for them. I hoped that I could be one of those people. As adults living in today's world we all have the obligation of being good role models, loving caregivers, and appropriate providers for our children. It isn't optional; it's mandatory and a privilege.

There are moments in life that can't be explained. I also believe that there are choices you make in life that completely end up defining you. Deciding to work in the PICU was one of those choices for me. It's where this tale really begins and where my love for connecting with people really starts. The things I learned there, the people I met, the families I took care of (that took care of me), and the experiences I had are the reasons I am where I am today. They're why I believe in what I believe in, and why I continue to work in pediatric health care.

Part 2

BEDSIDE

Chapter 9

Recognizing Emotional Needs

I've come to realize an inalienable truth: connection is essential to meaningful experiences. In my learning about how to develop a powerful connection, something dawned on me. I've never maintained a good relationship with a relative, developed a friendship, learned adequately from a teacher, had a meaningful interaction with a stranger, really taken care of a patient, or been able to grow as a husband/father without putting forth effort to build/sustain it. Think of any experience in your life where connecting with another person meant something to you. Would it have meant as much if the effort were poor?

Bedside nursing was a natural testing ground for this theory. Especially because the ability to build a connection vastly depended on my willingness to put forth the effort, and the more effort I was willing to exert the stronger the connection I was able to establish. Patients and their caregivers are in an extremely vulnerable state, where they are craving warmth, trust, and partnership. Interactions are very fragile and if navigated the wrong way can create a relationship that's neither beneficial for me nor the patient. If navigated the wrong way, it can cause issues that may inhibit the care for that shift, maybe even the care for multiple shifts to come.

When I first started as a nurse in the intensive care unit, a vast majority of my energy was exerted on navigating the art of multitasking, figuring out a system on how to multitask appropriately, and not screwing up. In the beginning, and in that rabbit hole, it was easy to forget about the emotional needs of the patient/family. When I first started as that new nurse in the PICU, I tried not to lose sight of the importance of establishing effective trust with the patient/family/caregiver. I had learned a lot in nursing school about how much benefit comes from exerting specific effort towards emotional connection. Therefore I attempted different strategies with not only families, but also with patients.

The moment I walk into a room at 7:30 a.m. during any given shift, the opportunity to create a connection is immediately available. No matter what happened in the previous shift or days leading up to it, the slate at that moment was clean. Immediately upon walking into the room, I made a conscious effort to establish myself as a caring, trustworthy partner. An effort to show that I was there to help that child heal and walk out of that room. Part of establishing that, and a strategy that I always started with, was assessing the situation.

How long have they been here? What kind of night did they have?

What needed to be done for that day (i.e. a trip to radiology, lots of labs, IV dressing changes, baths, medications, etc.)?

How chatty or how interested in chatting was the family?

Have their needs been met well or not so well up to this point in the stay?

A common next step for me after assessing the room was to use a bit of humor. It's a good way to break the ice as well as further your assessment of the situation. It can be tricky because it's very subjective, but typically well received as long as it's done tastefully. I always erred on the side of corny and basic "dad jokes." In many cases I'd write on the room whiteboard a standard joke of the day: "Why do pilgrims' pants always fall down? Because they wear their belt buckles on their hats." Simple.

I've certainly had my days where I didn't want to put forth an effort to connect and care on a deeper level. These days are generally forgettable because I'm in there doing my job and completing my tasks like a robot. I've missed many opportunities this way; missed chances to improve someone's day on, quite possibly, the worst day of their life. I found that if I conducted myself this way I never established a meaningful connection. Furthermore, too many people get comfortable with this approach because it doesn't require you come out of your zone.

I took care of an adult patient with a pediatric type of cancer once. The patient was actually married, and his wife stayed in the hospital room every night. I took care of them multiple days in a row and got to know them well over that time period. It was different, being able to have "adult" conversations with a patient, but it was refreshing as well. Through that, I learned he was a big movie fan and, furthermore, appreciated great movie scores (essentially soundtracks). This immediately connected us and henceforth brought us closer together. On the way home after my first shift with him, his situation occupied a lot of my thoughts. I thought about how difficult it would be (he and I were about the same age, and both newly married) to live in a hospital with such a debilitating disease. How difficult it must be for his wife to see him like that day in and day out. The conversations and connection we shared led me to want to do something more for him over upcoming shifts.

What would I want in this situation? The answer was relatively simple: something to distract my mind from what was physically happening around me.

The next day I brought in three movies from my collection at home: *The Good, Bad, and the Ugly*; *Good Will Hunting*; and *Road to Perdition*. All three are phenomenal flicks and all three have very memorable scores. I thought this would help bring a little distraction and maybe a little joy to his situation. He was appreciative of the effort and proceeded to watch the movies throughout the course of the day. Luckily for me, it was a Saturday and relatively calm on the unit, so I was able to enjoy it with him here and there.

I highlight that story for no reason other than the fact that it took very little additional effort to connect with him on a deeper level. Just recognition of what he may possibly need. It was extremely simple to carry out but the recognition of the need had to be there. At this point in my nursing journey I had conditioned myself to spot emotional needs of patients, and because of that my perception of how much effort I had to exert, changed. It took deliberate practice on a daily basis but the connections created, developed, and maintained because of this conditioning have been both humbling and fruitful.

Chapter 10

Hugs Are Crucial

A mother, a wife, a basketball coach, a leader. Those labels are just a few ways to describe the family member of a patient whose list of barriers/challenges is anything but short. She's the mother of a 13-year-old boy with Angelman syndrome. Angelman syndrome is a neurogenic disorder that is often misdiagnosed as cerebral palsy or autism. The syndrome is characterized by developmental delay, seizures, aphasia, and gait instability. He is developmentally similar to a 3-year-old child except that he is nonverbal. He's also built like a defensive lineman, which only amplifies the complexity of his care. His resilience and her perseverance are incredible. We all spent a significant amount of time together while he navigated his way through three separate admissions, pancreatitis, and septic shock.

He initially was brought to the emergency department because he had epigastric abdominal discomfort (as evidenced by his localization of pain to the affected area), constipation, and dehydration in the preceding 12 hours. While in the emergency department he received fluids and medications for pain. The pancreas was not well visualized during abdominal sonography because of the patient's inability to cooperate and gaseous distention. Consequently, contrast-enhanced computed tomography (CT) was performed and showed a mildly edematous pancreas and inflammation reflecting pancreatitis. While he was still in the emergency department, blood samples were obtained for various laboratory studies, and serum levels of amylase and lipase were the most abnormal values.

The clinical features, elevated levels of pancreatic enzymes, and CT results suggested acute pancreatitis, and he was admitted to the gastrointestinal unit for further management of dehydration, pain, and diet. After four days, a repeat CT showed an edematous pancreas with no fluid collection and no evidence of necrosis or abscess. He was showing marked clinical improvement and after 11 days in the hospital he was discharged home. I didn't have any interaction with this patient or his family during this admission, but this was just the beginning.

Approximately seven months later, the boy was again brought to the emergency department. At the time of admission and according to his family, he had diaphoresis, abdominal and lower back pain, diarrhea, and vomiting. Vital signs were even more abnormal than those at the first admission.

While in the emergency department, he received fluids, medication for the nausea and vomiting, and medications for pain. A CT scan showed a prominently edematous pancreas with possible necrotizing pancreatitis. Additionally, an area of localized fluid was noted at the lesser sac near the pancreatic body, suggestive of a pancreatic pseudocyst. His serum levels of amylase and lipase were markedly elevated. His clinical features, CT results, and elevated enzyme levels led to a diagnosis of acute pancreatitis complicated by a pseudocyst. A rare but significant event with many complications in pediatric patients.

Because of treatments received in the emergency department and the clinical signs and symptoms, physicians decided to admit him to the pediatric intensive care unit (PICU). Admission to the unit was warranted because of respiratory distress related to fluid overload during correction of dehydration and the increasing need for sedation. His escalating aggression and agitation most likely were due to confusion (a result of his neurological disorder) and pain. This highlights significant clinical findings present on admission to the PICU.

This is where we met and started our journey together. He showed further hemodynamic instability, respiratory distress, persistent hyperthermia, and a combined respiratory-metabolic acidosis. The pseudocyst was the assumed culprit for all of the complications; however, his condition needed to be stabilized before the pseudocyst could be addressed. A chest radiograph showed atelectasis and pulmonary edema. The radiographic findings, results of blood gas analysis, and the clinical signs and symptoms were enough for elective intubation to provide better airway management. He was treated with adult-dosage intravenous infusions of pain and sedation medications for airway management. He had a persistent fever and was treated with cooling blankets and scheduled doses of Tylenol. He had elevated blood sugar levels so a continuous infusion of insulin was started too.

In the PICU, two central venous catheters were placed. Central venous access was needed for continuous sedation, antibiotic therapy, nutrition, and sporadic use of drugs to regulate blood pressure. He was unable to tolerate oral feedings, necessitating placement of a post pyloric nasal tube and continuous feedings. A nasogastric tube was also placed for continuous gastric decompression.

All of this paints a picture of a complex patient where a well-organized team and meticulous medical management becomes key. The physician/nurse dyad is important but the necessary involvement of family, and this mom in particular, became paramount. She was there every step of the way, taking notes, asking questions, suggesting little things that could be done for his comfort, was involved in all medical rounds, and was a delight to interact with. Her competence was off the charts. We talked about her son's care, yes, but we also connected on other things like family, her past life as a basketball coach, and future aspirations. We would even do a joke of the day on the room whiteboard as a way to cope with the current high stress situation. Little things like that seem to help families deal with a situation and an environment that's completely foreign.

I remember one day, about midway through the shift, her son was emerging from sedation. Again, his developmental age and massive size made conventional methods of management obsolete. She recognized his delicate state and immediately informed me. As I was walking toward the bed I noticed his arm breakaway from the soft-wrist restraints and swiftly move in the direction of his breathing tube. I literally "supermaned" over top of his torso and tried to hold his arms down. His mom did the same over his legs. Walking by, you would've thought we were trying to get a "3-count" pin in a wrestling match. I called toward the front desk,

"Is anyone available to bring PRN sedation? WE NEED HELP IN HERE!"

Within minutes a couple of other nurses came in and pushed some additional medications to help calm him. He was thrashing and wiggling hard but within seconds the meds kicked in, de-escalating the situation. His mom was at a breaking point. This was a couple of weeks into his care, little progress had been made, and seeing her son struggle through this became too much. I wasn't sure what else to do so I did the first thing that came to mind.

"Do you need a hug?"

Tears started to flow down her face and an affirming nod accompanied. She was one of the strongest parents I've ever encountered, but everyone has a breaking point and people need hugs sometimes. That moment was special to both us.

After 15 days of the aforementioned treatments, his condition finally became stable enough for us develop a plan of attack for this pseudocyst. Care providers from the institution's interventional radiology, gastroenterology, and critical care medicine were consulted about it. Because severe pancreatitis and its complications are not often problems at pediatric institutions, the gastroenterology team at a neighboring hospital for adults was also consulted. After much debate, the teams agreed to use interventional radiology to place an external drain in the pseudocyst/pancreas. After placement of the drain, his persistent fevers, abdominal distention, pain and agitation, and hyperglycemia markedly decreased.

During the next three months, he required three more admissions to the PICU. The main clinical problems in each readmission were pain, increased output from the external pancreatic drain, agitation, insulin maintenance, and diet management. Difficulty in diet management (feeding through a gastrojejunal tube) was a marked problem mainly because of his developmental level. His family managed the problem by keeping him on a strict feeding regimen via the gastrojejunal tube while allowing minimal oral intake. The pseudocyst continued to produce output for three months after insertion of the drain. The drain was subsequently removed via interventional radiology during the second readmission; it had been in the pseudocyst for 56 days. After the third readmission, his family was able to manage his home hydration, pain management, and low-fat diet regimen adequately.

To date, he continues to be fed through the gastrojejunal tube and is receiving oral antihyperglycemics daily for control of the diabetes associated with chronic pancreatitis and pseudocyst formation. However, his hospital admissions have decreased in frequency, suggesting that the disease process is being successfully managed at home.

His story and our connection come with a very clinical spin. The complexity involved with his care is just a drop in the bucket as to what bedside clinicians see day in and day out. The addition of engaged and competent families to the care team can't be stressed enough. Their involvement is crucial, as there truly is a direct correlation between successful patient outcomes and family engagement. The connection that is or isn't shared between them and the bedside staff acts as a catalyst to that success as well. I think our team (his mother at the head) and the bond we shared significantly aided in his successful turnaround. At the heart of it all was the love she had for her son.

Note from the patient's family:

It happened over nine years ago but in our minds and with every breath it is as if it happened yesterday. We experienced an awakening or surprised diagnosis of pancreatitis in September 2011. The events that brought our son to the ICU on his third admission to the local pediatric hospital are astonishing in themself. That day quickly deteriorated into a mirror of doctors introducing themselves and then going into total professionalism of getting me up to speed on the gravity of our son's situation. He was diagnosed with "Acute Pancreatitis" and "Pseudocysts." They needed to intubate him in order to get total control of his bodily functions while he and they fought off the septic shock. "Septic shock," I said out loud in my head. "I am going to lose my son tonight. I am mercifully helpless." It was all happening so fast. I know I did not sleep that night at all nor the next day. The ICU nurses were unbelievable and reassuring me that he was beginning to stabilize. He was experiencing hiccups in response to the treatment by the medical care team as he fought to survive.

Our son's nurse was the lifeline that I needed in order to balance the world that was continuing to go on outside the window in our room. He took time to explain the actions he was performing as he provided extremely great care for our son. He noticed small changes in his body from color, temperature, and limb size, as well as many other changes.

He combined his observation skills with the instruments controlling his body functions to keep him in a safe medical state while his body continued to fight for survival. One day into the second week of this experience, a plan to battle for Derek emerged. The gastrointestinal doctors who specialize in pancreatitis at neighboring adult facility and our pediatric institution worked together to figure out the best treatment for a positive outcome for our son. Even the best thought-out plans were constantly changing due to Derek's medical state. He was making it extremely challenging for the entire team. During this second week, we took several road trips from the ICU to radiology for MRI and CT exams. This was to determine the extent of the situation they were facing with the pancreas. They discovered the pseudocyst had grown considerably in size and time was no longer on my son's side. They were not sure why he developed a fever that each day grew higher than the day before until it was at 105 degrees. This rise in temperature occurred with two cooling blankets to aid in bringing the temperature down. The window to practice medicine was closing and steps needed to be taken to rule out the possible suspects from his head to his toes. The nurse was by my side through this process and gave me confidence to advocate for my son. He gave a human touch of compassion to myself and my husband and our other two sons who came and visited their brother. He bonded with our other two sons and helped them to grasp the events that were happening to their brother.

One day I was talking about our son's disability and how I was beginning to feel so helpless and unattached from this world. He stood next to me and said, "Do you need a hug?" I quietly said yes and began to cry unashamedly. The hug he gave me was more than great medicine—it was a lifeline that brought me back to the living, for I was on autopilot from the day we came into the hospital and I had not actually breathed. I now felt alive again and empowered to fight even more for his life!

A new plan was designed and as the days wore on, our son slowly came back to us. We knew we would be forever changed by this event and our life has a new normal with a greater purpose and extended family members. The debt of appreciation could never be measured with silver or gold. The hug and display of humility, humanity, and support to our son and family can never be repaid or valued to any measurement on earth.

Chapter 11

Smile Anyway

It's daybreak and I'm trapped behind enemy lines. The hisses of live rounds continue to whizz by and the smell of a heated battle fills the air. I have nowhere to go and am barricaded by little cover. The only thing I have is my trusty sidearm and the only hope is to fight my way out. I take a few deep breaths and decide it's time.

"AHHHHH!!!!"

I quickly somersault to the right while firing off two shots. Both miss the mark. Suddenly, a feeling of remorse rushes over me as I have nowhere to hide and the safe zone appears miles away. The scream from my enemy is deafening and demoralizing. Death seems imminent. It's almost as if he knew how desperate I was and expected my offensive approach. Knowing I have no place left to hide, he lets off several rounds as well.

"I'm HIT!!"

One well-aimed shot dismantles my leg and I hit the ground with undeniable force. Bloodied and unable to move, my enemy shows no mercy. He hovers over my mangled body with a mischievous smile. I try to crawl away but the effort is futile.

"Any last words?"

Before I have any time to speak he fired a single shot straight into my back.

Everything goes black.

This is the imaginary world Jordan and I lived in every day together. He's six-years-old with an extraordinarily complex medical history. One that includes Congenital Diaphragmatic Hernia, Pulmonary Hypertension, and Short Gut Syndrome. This disease has put him through 87 surgical procedures, multiple ICU stays, and kept him in the hospital four years out of his six. Turning his ICU room into a battlefield and playing war was one of our favorite games. The kid had an arsenal of Nerf guns available at the bedside. When he wasn't taking me prisoner (or rather taking no prisoners), we'd draw massive targets on his room door and fire Nerf bullets; keeping tallies of who hit the most bulls eyes. We'd also play baseball or race cars on PlayStation. This was all when we could actually find some downtime from when we weren't managing the care of his very complex condition.

Jordan's what we like to call a "frequent flyer." He's always in the hospital and frequently transfers to the ICU. In his case, it was because he would constantly develop bloodstream infections from his bowel contents not emptying properly. He had multiple fistulas and stomas protruding from his abdomen that leaked stool. After so long the contents would "pool" and eventually find ways into the blood. Those infections would lead to respiratory problems, which often required endotracheal tube placement and ventilator support for days to weeks. This vicious cycle would repeat itself over and over again which, unfortunately, meant that any more than one or two weeks at home was rare.

All of this begins with a Congenital Diaphragmatic Hernia, which is a defect in the diaphragm. The diaphragm, which is composed of muscle and other fibrous tissue, separates the organs in the abdomen from those in the chest. Abnormal development of the diaphragm before birth leads to defects ranging from a thinned area in the diaphragm to its complete absence. Jordan's case exhibited a complete absence. Because of this, he had to have multiple procedures done that eventually resulted in Short Gut Syndrome as well. It's a malabsorption disorder caused by a lack of functional small intestine. It poses a multitude of issues for your gastrointestinal system, many of which you and I take for granted. Furthermore, all of these surgeries took a toll.

Whenever a patient undergoes surgery, someone from the surgery team comes to the family to explain procedure logistics and review potential risks. The more invasive the procedure, the higher the risk; however, in most cases the risks are minimal. None of the procedures Jordan underwent seemed to go his way. They always seemed to leave things more complicated than before. Hence, he ended up with three different stomas protruding from his abdomen following a final surgery where the gastrointestinal surgeons thought they could fix everything. It was worth a shot but once again, Jordan proved more complex than most others. I prefer to call him unique. Nonetheless, during this time period is where our paths connected.

It was the first day after that final surgery. He was intubated on a ventilator and had bags upon bags plus bandages covering his entire abdomen. At the time he had pain medicine infusing but it was at a very low rate. Jordan's one of the only children I ever took care of that could calmly remain awake, interact, and even smile while a tube was down his throat. His pain threshold was off the charts for someone of his age and experience. The biggest challenge was figuring out how to manage his abdominal abnormalities and complexity. Trying to come up with a system where his bowel contents didn't leak all over his skin and require two-hour bag/ bandage changes was difficult. His family proved to be the game changer in that regard.

As a nurse you are constantly warned about challenges that arise in patient/family dynamics. At the end of any shift handoff there's always time reserved to discuss any social issues and what to expect. Jordan, as mentioned, was a frequent flyer, so his family was well known across the ICU staff. In handoff during that first shift, the night shift nurse told me that this family could be a little particular (who wouldn't after four years in and out of hospitals?). I always took these types of comments with a grain of salt because, in my experience, as long as you introduce yourself, communicate effectively, and put forth effort there generally was never a problem. Jordan's mom wasn't there the first day I cared for him but we did run into a dressing change emergency where I had to call her. She was extremely helpful. She explained things well and helped advocate for Jordan in a way that he desperately needed. We established an immediate connection and never looked back.

I decided to sign up as Jordan's primary nurse after those first few days together. The bond we established was incredible. He stayed in the ICU for a couple of months after that final surgery but would intermittently come back in stretches of days-to-weeks, and we'd pick up right where we left off. He had this thing where he wouldn't talk or smile for the first several hours up to even a day after an ET tube would be removed. It took me a long time to figure out what his weakness was but finally I did: annoyance. I'd walk in there and start doing my job, nonchalantly, and continuously ask:

"Jordan......what are you doing??"

The first several times he would just look up with "what do you mean, what am I doing" eyes (since he couldn't go anywhere). Then finally, by like the eighth time, he'd always reply with a loud but semi-playful,

"NOTHING!!!"

It was definitely just so I'd shut up.

This kid's courage was inspirational. He'd come back to the hospital, go to the floor, and come back to the ICU with a smile, every time. He took everything we had to throw at him and would keep moving, never giving up. No depression. No complaints. Just courage and positivity. It's because of that we decided to partner up and start a fundraiser together.

I love endurance sports; marathons, triathlons, you name it. A year after I met Jordan, I registered and began a 37-week training program for a full Ironman (2.4 mile swim, 112 mile bike, 26.2 mile run). Jordan, his family, and I joined together in an effort to raise money for a family assistance fund. This would provide financial aid to families of chronically ill children for such expenses as meals, gas, lodging, bus/taxi fare, etc.... The hospital got involved, we were able to get a local daycare involved, and Jordan's family even sponsored a softball tournament to help raise money. It was going incredibly well and he was a fantastic advocate for it.

Then, a month before the race, I received a call from his mom.

"He's not doing well. We were just admitted for palliative care. You should come see him as soon as you can."

He had gotten another infection that he just couldn't recover from and his system had reached its limit. It wasn't looking good. The palliative care team kept him as comfortable as they could and he eventually passed away the next day. I remember looking at him as it was all happening and my thoughts gravitated to how hard his life had been. He was extremely loved but physically, what a challenge. That thought, though, didn't last long. He wouldn't let it. My tears went away and an incredible calm arrived, like nothing I'd ever felt before. His body, lying there in that hospital bed, exuded peace. He was relaxed, he was painless, and he was free. Everyone was sad, yes, as a bright light from this world had just gone out, but his legacy lived. His strength was infectious and it was real. It was something to believe in.

A couple of days later I did something I never thought I'd have to do in my lifetime. I gave a eulogy at a six-year-old's funeral. He was beautiful, and the support around him was magical. The place was jam-packed with people and his casket was completely decked out in Red's apparel. The loss was difficult as I wanted nothing more than for him to look up at me and smile. His memory continued on though and his presence was continually felt. The Ironman was a couple of weeks later and I finished in twelve hours. I really struggled during the second half of the marathon leg of the race. General fatigue/weakness set in and my head was a mess. I found myself constantly calling on Jordan for help and strength. The finish wasn't pretty but I managed to muster up enough "pep" to stride out the last few hundred meters. The finish line itself was emotional as there's no doubt in my mind that he helped me through the entire thing. We were also able to raise almost six thousand dollars for the family-assist fund. All because a little boy continued to fight the good fight. Sometimes when you think you're down and out it helps to close your eyes, remember why you're doing what you're doing, smile, and power through. The results always surprise me.

Note from the patient's family:

From the moment we found out that there could be something wrong with him, we knew he would be special. He came into this world six weeks early and stole our hearts with his very first cry. He was a beautiful little boy with 10 fingers and 10 toes and let the world know things would be his way when he immediately peed on the doctor.

The first four months we bonded with him in the NICU. It's hard not to have your baby home with you and leave Jordan every night. He gave us many scares, but he proved to everyone that he was a fighter. Everyone fell in love with him as he had a smile that would light up the world. He stole the hearts of everyone he met. He never knew a stranger and wanted to talk and play with everyone. The hospital was a second home to him, and it created a second family for us. He would get so excited when his favorite doctors and nurses were on duty because he knew it would play time.

He loved his family and absolutely loved baseball. He was a huge Reds fan. When he was home, we would spend hours playing wiffle ball. He would pretend to be all the Reds players and run the bases as fast as his little legs would go (pulling his oxygen lines behind him). If he was in the hospital, we would watch and re-watch every game, then take bets on the outcome with his nurses and doctors. Predictions were written on the whiteboard and the winner got his stash of play money. Of course, like all little kids, he did not like to lose.

He is what is important in life. He taught us to accept people as they are and that not everyone's the same. That family is everything and you stick together through fun times and hard times. Finally, that spending time with him was a very special gift.

He will always be missed but we know that he is in heaven playing baseball; running the bases without any pain or any of the restrictions he had on earth. We know that every time the wind blows, it's him whispering love into our ear and every time thunder rumbles or lighting lights up the sky, it's him smashing a home run. He's with us every day and we thank GOD that he was given to us for the most amazing 6 ½ years.

Chapter 12

Be Annoyingly Persistent

The healthcare field is a tough environment across the board. Consumers are faced with a multitude of barriers ranging from astronomical costs, to issues with literacy, to the risk of obtaining hospital acquired conditions—just to name a few. As someone who's dedicated their life to that field, I am aware of what other challenges are on the other side of the coin. The days are long, hospitals are open 24/7/365, and it's non-profit, so promotions are sparse and raises minimal. That's all without saying the daily dealings with death/dying, more bodily fluids than you knew existed, and sometimes patient or family aggression, which are frequent aspects of the job. Furthermore, egos run amuck within hospitals walls, and you think that being "wrong" isn't an option, or at least that's the perception.

If you look at the educational background of most doctors and nurses, you'll find that they have usually excelled academically. They graduated high school with high GPA or honors, and carried that work ethic into college. In order to get into any competitive nursing program or medical school, you have to be at the top of the academic ladder and in most cases, you have to maintain that mentality in order to remain in those programs and schools, and then graduate. It can be cutthroat. Now take all of these intelligent people that have been led to believe that they can't fail or be wrong, and put them into the same place. There's your hospital staff, in a place where an unwavering ego can get someone in big trouble. Luckily, this hospital supports psychological safety, which is helpful in a case where speaking up is a necessity.

Several years ago a little boy was at a laser tag establishment for a birthday party. He's a normal, healthy boy running around with his friends and having a blast. Suddenly, he is found on the ground twitching and unresponsive. No one saw anything happen and he had no pre-existing health conditions. The presumption is that he hit his head, had a seizure, and fell to the ground. The strange part is that only his left side was twitching (face, arm, and leg). Paramedics are called and he's immediately taken to the hospital emergency room. He was given a lot of seizure medication and had to have a tube placed for breathing assistance. He was stabilized in the trauma bay and sent to the ICU. After a multitude of tests, it was discovered that he had a middle cerebral artery infarct. The MCA is the vessel most commonly associated with cerebrovascular accidents (strokes), which would explain why his left side was affected with twitching. This is a pretty rare occurrence in children, but ultimately that part of his brain had suffered ischemia for reasons unknown. A couple of days later, he had improved enough to have the breathing tube taken out and sedation medications removed. It was now time to try and start recovery with less intensive treatment.

One night soon after, I was working and taking care of this little guy. At this point he was about seven days out from the accident but was being monitored closely in the ICU still. When these types of events occur usually there is about a seven-day period where the patient is most at risk for tertiary swelling to the brain because of the injury. During this time, patients need ICU attention solely because of that risk as brain swelling usually results in bad outcomes. He was at the tail end of this window and seemingly out of the woods. He was my only patient at the time and I was open for an additional admission, if one arose.

Everything was pretty consistent and stable through the first round of assessments. He was responsive enough for what I'd expect for that kind of injury: had some left-sided weakness and was showing some signs of withdrawal (shaking, low-grade fever, lack of attention) from being on continuous sedation medications for several days. Soon after that first round, though, came an unexpected vomiting episode, as well as a slight decline in his responsiveness. He had no such events during the day so this immediately raised a red flag for me and my gut told me something could be seriously wrong. I called the doctor on my team and explained the situation:

"He had a vomiting episode and a slight change in neuro status. Can you come check him out and see if a CT scan is in order?"

The doctor came to the bedside and did his assessment:

"It's just withdrawal symptoms. I don't think he needs a scan."

I thought that was an under-reaction but carried on with my duties. Thirty minutes later, a second episode of vomiting occurred and further decline in responsiveness. Now I was really worried as this is looking consistent with possible brain swelling. That type of disease escalation can lead to significant issues, possibly death.

"He vomited again," I said, "and he seems to be declining more neurologically. I really think we need to get a scan and see what's going on here."

The doctor came to the bedside again.

"It's just withdrawal. I'm not ordering a scan."

Upset with this decision and knowing, in my gut, that there's much more going on in this boy's body, I insisted with another call and push.

"Something is very wrong here. He's vomited twice in an hour, which he hasn't done all day, has declining neuro status, and decreasing reactions. We need to scan this kid."

After this third push, the tired, reluctant, and now pissed doctor ordered the scan. We rushed down, were able to obtain the scan, and came back up to the unit without any further incident. Throughout this whole process, the boy's family, who had already been through a shell-shocking event, continued to become more and more worried. They're a loving, caring family with a couple of other children, well educated, but increasingly confused. They had a hard time comprehending all of the issues, as they were told: seven days and he should be in the clear. I became much acquainted with them throughout this whole process and tried to communicate, very clearly, what was happening.

It wasn't long after we came back from the scanner that the same doctor who ordered the test arrived at the bedside with a report on the results.

"He's had increased swelling to the injured, infarcted area and his brain has shifted across the midline of his skull. We need to take him to surgery immediately."

The mad rush of preparation for surgery began instantaneously. The neurosurgery team was setting up the operating room as this conversation with the family was happening. The doctor, ICU charge nurse, and I didn't waste another minute getting the patient packed up and ready for transport downstairs. We did our best to explain what all of this meant to a very emotional family, but they knew how serious this was by the hasty movements of our actions. The OR nurses and doctors were upstairs within ten minutes for handoff and consent. Then, before we knew what happened, he had left the unit, his fate now up to the knowledge and skills of the neurosurgeon.

I'm no smarter or wiser than any other clinician, but I know when my gut is telling me something is wrong. Instincts are innate, powerful, and mostly right. Trusting them is hard. Sticking up for them is harder. After the dust had settled post transport to the OR, I walked directly past the doctor who continued to delay the ordering of that scan. We made clear-cut eye contact and no words were said. No admission of a mistake and no apology. Also, no I-told-you-so.

That patient ended up getting half of his skull removed (craniotomy) to allow his brain room to swell. He was admitted back into the ICU postoperatively, needing a breathing tube and intracranial monitoring probe (ICP) for an additional week. It's very possible, and probably likely, that had he not gone to surgery that night, we would have been calling his time of death by the morning. He's alive and well today but had to endure extensive rehabilitation to obtain motor functionality back. He still needs rehab and isn't back to 100% normality, but things could have gone so much worse.

Bottom line, trust yourself, and in what you believe is right. You never know when it could save a life, possibly even your own.

Note from the patient's family:

I never really believed that old saying that your life could change in the blink of an eye until it happened to my family. One minute I had a healthy little boy running and playing with his friends and before I could catch my breath, that same little boy was fighting for his life. The next few weeks were very overwhelming and it seemed like every day the story changed. My son seemed to follow every worst-case scenario. At one point we were told he would never walk or talk again. That there was a very good chance he would spend the rest of his days in a vegetative state. The night he had his emergency craniotomy was the worst night of my life. I remember praying to God to take my boy if he really would not have any quality of life, and I can tell you those were the most difficult prayers to ever leave my lips. But today he is our miracle. He attends high school and spends his days with his peers. My son not only walks and talks, he types and can do Algebra. He has dreams of college and a career in business. My son is my hero. He walks through life with a smile on his face and love in his heart despite the incredible obstacles that have been placed in front of him. He makes me proud every single day and he surprises me with his accomplishments almost as often. Yes, my son has challenges and deficits, but he continues to move forward eight years after his strokes. With all he has been through, he has taught me so much and that gives me hope through my sorrow.

The following chapters have details that have been changed for the protection of the patients and families.

Chapter 13

Pay Attention

Suicide is an ongoing problem in today's world. As if the rates among adults weren't already prevalent and tragic enough, the rates among children are shocking. In America, we've seen the youth (ages 5-24) suicide total increase from 5,265 in 2013 to 6,156 in 2016 . That's a trend we can't be okay with, a trend that demands action. As adults, it's not just our opportunity, it's our obligation to connect with these young people. Death is an inevitable truth in life and it's one I've begun to accept as I not only evaluate my own mortality but also by experiencing it second hand on the job. Self-inflicted death is something I'll never be able to accept, though.

One day I arrived at work. I was on night shift at the time, and right away upon arrival, I saw that my bedside assignment was a 17-year-old with an anoxic (lack of oxygen) brain injury. I didn't immediately assume attempted suicide, but that type of diagnosis is never a promising one. When I got to the bedside, the child was mostly unresponsive to stimulus and was on a ventilator, connected to a tube helping to breathe. There was a medication infusing to help with blood pressure and another to help with brain swelling. We were also utilizing a protocol that employed specific techniques intended to reduce significant stress experienced by the body.

Because of the lack of oxygen to the brain, the body was under an enormous amount of stress and the nervous system was beginning to shut down. The family was just like most families who have ever been in this type of situation: hysterical. They didn't understand how this could happen, didn't understand how this child could have done this, and most of all, they blamed themselves. They were a very loving family and loved their child immensely. It was very apparent in all their interactions. I was able to connect with them right away.

Throughout the course of the night, I talked to them, listened to them, cried with them, and tried to care for their child as best I could. During all of this time with them I learned how everything happened. It was because of bullying. Having never experienced anything like this before and not knowing how to self-regulate all of these emotions, the child saw no other way out and decided to attempt a hanging. The siblings were first on the scene, attempted CPR, and called the life squad.

When put into situations like this, it is difficult to know what to say, what to do. Even this early in my career, I had seen suicide attempts before; it's the nature of working in a busy ICU, in a big city, and being a part of the nursing profession. They're always tough to swallow and each comes with their fair share of different challenges. However, this experience was different. This child had done something I had not seen before and it was as profound as anything I had ever witnessed.

When I did the first full body assessment at the start of my shift that night, I noticed five distinct scratch marks on both cheeks of the face directing diagonally away from the eyes. This led me to one gut-wrenching, inalienable conclusion: regret and panic. An attempt was made to try and take the wire off after the choice had already been made, but it was too late. The horrifying reality of regret in making a choice based off of impulsive emotion. The choice had been made and nothing could be done to take it back, changing the child's life and the lives of loved ones forever.

Despite everyone's best efforts that night, this child wasn't able to pull through, and there was nothing anyone could do. The brain had endured too much and due to the condition, the family had to make the decision to withdraw life support. They decided to end the suffering. It was one of the first deaths I had ever seen. Watching a family go through that experience is something you don't ever really get used too. It never becomes just "part of the job," and it becomes something you never want to personally experience.

I wish I could've talked to this child and explained that things will get better. It seems like they won't, and that there's no other way, but this too shall pass. It's really hard for teenagers to see this because of the volatility of their emotions, especially when something like bullying occurs. A major strength and weakness of the human race is our experience with emotions. They are the complete basis of connection and are the reason we are the way we are, but why?

Basic emotions are naturally occurring responses to a situation. Everything you see, smell, hear, taste, and touch travels through your body in the form of electric signals. These signals pass from cell to cell until they reach their ultimate destination: your brain. They enter your brain at the base near the spinal cord, but must travel to your frontal lobe before reaching the place where rational, logical thinking takes place. The trouble is that these signals pass through your limbic system along the way— the place where emotions are produced. This journey ensures you experience things emotionally before your ability to reason can kick into gear. Trying to reason before you react emotionally takes a certain amount of self-awareness, maturity, and control because you're trying to change the way your body wants you to react. This is why the vast majority of teen suicide occurs with extreme haste. They emotionally respond to a breakup, a fight, an insult, or any number of negative stimuli that occur in a teenager's world, and make a very rash decision.

Emotions are experienced daily and they are powerful. They may signal a change in our environment, a change within us, or a change in both. They are generally fleeting, though, and are short term in comparison to other states of mind. Moods, for example, can last hours, days, or even weeks. Then there's our much more long-term, more innate personality, a lifelong set of traits that comprise our individual, predictable reactions to situations. So, as opposed to the last two, a function of an emotion is to get our attention and demand a response, immediately, before we get a chance to reason.

I emphasize other states of mind solely to make the point that emotions don't stick around long term. The way a person utilizes their emotions may be a personality trait but the bottom line is that emotions are immediate motivators. They motivate you to react, whether it be a good or bad reaction, before you have the time to reason. This is where human connection becomes unbelievably important. When a child experiences something negative or positive, how can we help motivate their reaction? I like to believe that it is by establishing great relationships centered on open communication and honesty. The hope being that if they feel like they can trust, confide in, and connect with you, then their first response will gravitate to the security of your relationship.

I wasn't able to consciously meet that child but we experienced an immense connection together. I also felt it with the family. There was a strong, unconditional love that was obviously apparent between them, and I truly believe that they shared the kind of relationship I just described. I remember standing at the bedside late during that night shift trying to do anything possible to help. I remember looking at the child's face in complete anguish, and stroking coarse hair to try and provide any kind of comfort. My immediate thought went to the scratch marks on the cheeks. The child couldn't vocalize it but I knew at that moment how much regret there was in making the choice that was made. They may have had that relationship, but it still comes down to a choice. That choice resulted in a loss that no parent should ever have to experience.

It wasn't until the end of my shift that they decided to withdraw care. When the process was completed and I was about to go home that morning, I decided to walk over to the parents. To this day, I struggle to find words for these types of situations and this moment wasn't any different. However, before I could say anything, the mom pulled me in close and gave me a hug that I'll never fully be able to describe. It was close, intimate, and mutually needed from two strangers who had become friends. It was the first time I truly realized what family-centered care meant.

As a pediatric nurse, I care for children, but in the same breath, I have to be a crutch for the parents. In a night as dark as that one, in the last place they'd ever want to be, those parents still found comfort in a connection with a complete stranger. I couldn't have been more willing to try and help shoulder their burden. It's a connection I'm grateful for, that meant a lot to me; I hope they felt the same.

Chapter 14

Love Always

What if you knew you only had days or weeks to live? Who would you want to spend that time with? How would you want to spend that time? Maybe you've thought about this kind of thing, maybe you haven't, but regardless, the answers are important. Unequivocally, life is finite and precious. As I've gotten older, the "who" in the above questions has become much more important to me than anything else. That also directly relates to the how. Life is better with other people and more importantly, with a partner. The ultimate connection; one, as we'll dive deeper into later, that has required more of me then I ever would have thought, but one that gives more than any other. This became apparent to me while caring for, in a rare occasion, someone that was older than me.

At thirty-five years old, I'm not sure anyone expects to spend most of his or her time in a hospital or hospital bed. That was the reality for Jim. He had been diagnosed with a gastrointestinal (belly) inflammatory pseudo tumor. This is an uncommon benign disease of unknown etiology (origin), mimicking malignancy both clinically and radiologically. These tumors are composed of fibrotic and necrotic tissue as well as various inflammatory cells (histiocytes, myofibroblasts, plasma cells, and lymphocytes). It's most common in children and adolescents and usually presents with diverse symptoms . Jim's mass covered the vast majority of his abdomen and compressed his aorta and esophagus. This caused severe and frequent cardiovascular and respiratory complications. He needed non-invasive mechanical ventilation support and nasogastric feeding. He often had to undergo a procedure that removes fluid from the belly in order to relieve pressure.

Simple things, like lying flat, were made difficult for Jim. He also couldn't enjoy the gratification of full meals or complete, deep breaths without support. This stuff didn't seem to get him down though. When I met Jim he was larger than life. He sported a positive, happy can-do attitude and smiled all the time. He also had the support of a loving fiancé and family. Something that you wouldn't have noticed with Jim is that his time was limited. The compression his mass was creating was occluding major blood vessels, making it incredibly difficult to breathe and circulate oxygenated blood to his body. Given that situation, it wasn't a matter of 'if' but 'when' the stress would be too much and he would code (essentially have a massive heart attack).

At a young age he was being faced with tough questions: *Is surgery on vital organs attached to a massive tumor worth the risk? Is resuscitation a good decision in a code situation?*

I don't think I would know what to say if faced with the same questions. One thing he did know was whom he wanted to spend the rest of his life with. Jim and his fiancé were in love and inseparable, there was no denying it. Their bond was so strong they decided to get married while Jim was hospitalized. There was a bachelor party (details unable to be disclosed) and a wedding in the hospital chapel. Jim was classed up in a bowtie and they had streamers attached to the back of his walker as they recessed out of the ceremony. I was lucky enough to witness, first hand, what love "in sickness and in health" looks like.

About two weeks after the wedding, Jim took a turn for the worst though. I had just come onto my night shift and was assessing him for the first time. As I walked in, he appeared to start having a panic attack, so we gave him some pain/anxiety medication to help calm him. It didn't work. He continued to deteriorate and became unresponsive and no family was in the room as they had just stepped out to go grab dinner. He never had made a firm decision on resuscitation so we did what we thought was clinically best and began CPR. I remember doing chest compressions and not wanting to stop. It seemed so unfair for this young man to have life cut so short. We kept trying and trying (fluid, epinephrine, calcium chloride, etc.) but nothing worked. About 20 minutes into the code, his wife came back and told us to stop. This isn't what or how he wanted to go; she knew that. It was tough for the whole team but we had to respect their wishes. Jim deserved that.

To this day, one of the things I continue to think about is whether he could feel or knew that was going to happen so he waited until his family was out of the room. Did he not want them to see him go through that? I can't say I would want mine to. Jim was a complete all-star and lived life to the fullest. He knew what he wanted, and even though he was limited by his surroundings, he spent his time with whom he wanted. He and his wife had an incredible connection, stayed together through thick and thin, and everyone around them was lucky to have witnessed it.

Chapter 15

Join Them

Sometimes we decide to leave people alone because we feel it's more beneficial for them. We think we're bothering them in times of distress so we walk away and say to ourselves, "They just need some space." I don't agree with this logic. I think we leave people alone because it's more difficult for us to join them.

Empathy is really challenging and it is something I've failed at many times. Instead of trying to be truly empathetic to a situation, I've always tried to solve the problem. There's a huge difference between being there for someone and attempting to tell someone what to do. It has taken me a long time to realize that people don't need me to solve their problems; they just need to know that they're not alone. They need to know that someone is there for them, even if it's only just to listen. It took a connection with a courageous eight-year-old boy suffering from scoliosis to teach me this lesson.

Scoliosis is a condition that causes the spine to turn sideways. The bones in the spine twist and turn to create a "C" or "S" shape, instead of the normal straight line down the middle of the back. It is rarely painful and can often go unnoticed if the curves are relatively small. However, if the curves are large enough, surgical intervention is often needed.

He had congenital scoliosis; his spinal bones did not fully form or fuse together prior to birth. His curvature was so severe surgery was necessary. He would need to undergo spinal fusion surgery, a procedure that straightens the curve and fuses the vertebrae together so that they heal into one single solid bone.

During the operation, the spinal bones that make up the curve are realigned and small pieces of bone (called bone grafts) are placed in the spaces between the vertebrae to be fused. Over time, the bones grow together similar to the way a broken bone heals. Metal rods are also typically used and placed to help hold the bones together until the fusion happens. The rods are attached to the spine by hooks, screws, and wires . This surgery usually takes between four and six hours, at which point the patient is transferred to an inpatient unit to recover.

An ICU admits a lot of patients post-operatively. Patients reside there, as opposed to a medical-surgical unit, because they need more astute observation and care. The nurse-patient ratios are lower in the ICU (1 RN to 1 patient or 1 RN to 2 patients) due to condition and acuity, so more attention can be given to the patient and their needs. This by no means suggests that ICU RN's are less busy; on the contrary, the amount of care ICU patients require give nurses in critical care settings MORE than enough to do. In fact, more often times than not, I wouldn't sit down or eat lunch until two or three o'clock in the morning or evening, which would be six or seven hours into my shift. That being clarified, it just so happened that Tim crossed my path during an evening shift while I was still in new hire RN orientation.

Things tend to move a little slower on night shift. There aren't as many people around, no massive teams of doctors rounding on patients, fewer patient admissions (typically), and it's just generally quieter. If your life can handle daytime sleep, I recommend it; it's definitely a more relaxed environment, and as shift work is concerned, more enjoyable. There's also more autonomy and need to access critical thinking skills more frequently when faced with acute physiological events. Surgical admissions don't occur often on p.m. shifts, but when they do, it's usually a case that takes a long time and was started in the afternoon. This patient had his spinal fusion scheduled late in the day, so his procedure was finished late evening.

When he came to the ICU, he wasn't actually going to be my patient; my preceptor and I already had a two-patient assignment so another nurse was admitting him. He came up around 11 p.m. Typically, when an RN gets a new admit, the surrounding "pod mates" chip in to help get the patient settled. That's exactly what we were doing as Tim rolled into the ICU on a Stryker bed frame.

Spinal Fusion patients used to be placed on a bed called a Stryker frame. It's a frame that secures the patient in position and permits turning in various planes without individual motion of parts (example following).

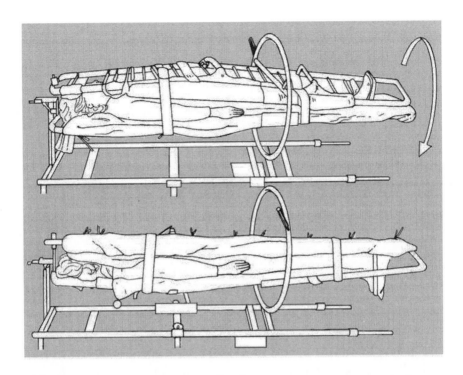

When the patient came to the ICU in this frame, he was facing the floor and was only with the surgical team. Standard protocol requires that a safe handoff occur between the ICU and surgery teams to ensure the best possible care for the patient. After handoff takes place, it's the ICU team's job to get the patient settled and resume care. We take vital signs, attach IV fluids, position equipment, and do an initial full-body assessment, among other things. When complex admissions like a spinal fusion are brought in, it usually takes multiple people to adequately complete all the necessary tasks. As our team was crossing things off the admission list, we heard Tim for the first time. His eyes were swollen shut due to the fluid shifts that occur during long surgeries and he was facing the floor. He had no family in the room as of yet and he was scared.

He cried out, "What's going on? I can't see anything?" He also couldn't move.

Imagine being eight-years-old, temporarily blind, scared, and trapped in that apparatus. Feeling so alone, he started crying and

81

didn't know what to do, as everyone in the room was focused in on their clinical duties at hand. At the time, I was helping obtain his vital signs and started to try and comfort him. Merely talking to him wasn't working though. He didn't know my voice, he couldn't see me, and he couldn't feel me. Why would a stranger saying that everything's going to be okay comfort his situation? Since words weren't working, I decided to do the only thing left I could try that may help. I joined him.

Without really thinking it through, I laid on the floor directly beneath him. His face was directly above mine and I could tell he was terrified. I reached upward and touched his face and spoke softly.

"I'm right here with you buddy, right beneath you. Don't be scared, your surgery is over and you're doing great."

More than anything, I wanted to make sure that he could feel my presence; I wanted to make sure that he knew he wasn't alone. It felt strange lying there on the hospital floor but in another way, it felt like the right thing to do. I actually told him that he could spit and it would hit me directly in the face. He didn't do it (which I was appreciative of) but nonetheless, the thought made him smile.

He did great after the surgery and was discharged home following the normal spinal fusion postoperative protocol. I've never seen or spoken to him since, and actually have no way of knowing whether or not laying on the floor beneath him that night helped. I hope that it did. I never did that with another patient.

This showed me that there's more to healing than just medicine; not everything can be dosed per kilogram and administered via IV. People, especially children, need to know that they're not alone; they need to feel connection and warmth. The human spirit thrives on interaction and taking the time to truly show you care can make all the difference in the world. Effort displays a willingness to go outside your comfort zone and say,

"I don't know exactly what you're going through, but I'm here if you need me."

Chapter 16

Learn From Failure

I've mentioned already how much I dislike making mistakes or failing; it's definitely been a learning process in my adult life. It's not because I see it as weakness or because I was pressured to succeed growing up. The reason is more so because of expectations. I set unrealistic expectations for myself and when I fall short of achieving my goal, I take it personally. When you take things personally, things get emotional, and then you tend to bear more burden than necessary. This has been an internal struggle. A strength in some ways but a weakness in many others. It's given me drive and motivation, but also contributed greatly to stubbornness, lack of humility, and to questioning whether I should actually take that risk of honesty.

When I first started out as a nurse I was confident. I thought I knew my stuff, couldn't be wrong, and couldn't make mistakes. Sound familiar? (Remember the previously mentioned proud and unyielding doctor.) I'd seen good success early on. I was able to take sicker patients with higher acuity and time manage pretty well, and quickly. I was very proud to be a nurse and proud to work in pediatrics. Talking to families and connecting with patients was by far my favorite part, but I also loved the critical-thinking and the problem-solving aspects. Sometimes I would just stand in a room, take a step back, and stare at the whole picture. Analyzing and monitoring vital sign trends, studying respiratory patterns on the ventilator, talking through potential adverse medication effects, and developing contingency plans in case something went wrong. It truly is a job where you can do something different every single shift.

On the other side of that love and confidence though was not wanting to admit to mistakes and not taking criticism well. Could it be just part of being young and immature? Possibly, but more likely, a character flaw.

One day shift soon after completing the six-month orientation, I was one-to-one with a reasonably sick patient. He was pretty busy from the get-go—intubated, lots of medications, and had a gastric tube. It was early on in the morning and things were steady. I wasn't in the weeds just yet but things had already begun to ramp up. All of the sudden, a swarm of clinicians appeared outside my door.

Day shift is a completely different environment from night shift, and one of the main differences is the workload that derives from physician rounds. This is when the group of ICU doctors (residents, fellows, and attendings) split up into teams and "round" to see every patient in the unit. The PICU is comprised of patients with all types of illnesses ranging from cancer, to respiratory illnesses (e.g. pneumonia), to endocrine diseases (e.g. diabetes), to trauma (e.g. car accidents/gunshots), among many others. Because of this, ICU doctors bring with them additional physicians from other specialty services from throughout the institution (depending on what type of illness the patient has). Pharmacists and dieticians also accompany the herd. If you have a patient with multiple anomalies, you could end up with 20 people in the hallway outside of the room. It's all necessary.

The round took about 15 minutes and came with 10 additional items for my work list. I'm a pretty old school, write-everything-down-on-a-list kind of a guy. Every nurse has their way of working and I was the kind that needed a checklist. I used to fold a piece of paper in half, write down every hour of the day, and then list all the tasks I needed to complete for each of those hours. As each task was completed, it earned a necessary "cross" through it. Rounds always threw wrenches into the system, and as a newer nurse, wrenches were still tough to juggle, especially on a busier day. Prioritization, at these times, becomes a crucial part of the job. You have to know what takes highest precedence and you have to be able to multitask effectively.

I never really liked asking for help, but something else that's difficult to learn is how to delegate tasks when you're in the weeds. I didn't do this very well either. So in the midst of all these additional tasks, plus all the other planned duties of the day, I started getting a little frantic. My room was messy and unorganized, and I was mixing tasks together in order to save time. However, what I was really doing was leaving tasks incomplete and creating more confusion. The recipe was beginning to spell disaster. I remember specifically prepping oral medications to administer via gastric tube while trying to talk to the family and chart all at the same time. Unfocused and distracted, I took all of those medications over to the bedside. I flushed the tube with sterile water and began giving medications one after the other. After I flushed everything through with another sterile water syringe, I took all of the empty syringes back over to the nurse's station to dispose of in the Sharps container. As I threw one syringe after another into the container I noticed that one was different than the rest. One looked like an IV Luer Lock syringe rather than the open tipped oral syringe that's used when giving oral medications.

"Shit, did I just give an IV med through the G-tube?!?!"

I immediately did an inventory of all my medications that were housed in the nurse server. One of the IV meds that was due later in the day had one missing. I definitely made a crucial mistake here. I hate to admit but the thought did cross my mind to not say anything. That's how much I didn't want to make mistakes. Then a flashback to my dad immediately surfaced, and I remembered a quote:

"Always take the risk of honesty."

There's protocol to follow as well as a hospital expectation when something like this happens. I had to tell my doctor team, fill out a hospital-wide safety incident report, and relay the news to the family. There's a "safety first" culture within the institution so I never felt like I was going to be punished for making a mistake but instead collaborated with to help mitigate potential future errors. My hesitance was mainly self-imposed. Thankfully, everything ended up being okay as nothing harmful happened to the patient; however, I was embarrassed. I was embarrassed more so because of how I'd been carrying myself as opposed to the mistake itself. I had been preoccupied with being successful and looking competent as a new nurse. I had been preoccupied with myself and had failed my patient because of it. I didn't give failure the necessary respect that it deserves, and thought I could do everything myself. That's a fool's mindset.

Never connecting with humility is dangerous. This was my wakeup call and opportunity to quit being stupid. There's no shame in asking for help and there's certainly nothing wrong with being careful. I had to learn this. I had to learn from this. I still wanted to succeed but I also realized that fearing failure wasn't a bad thing. Adequately fearing failure keeps you practicing, honing your skills, coming up with contingency plans, and always being prepared for battle.

Chapter 17

Comfortable Being Uncomfortable

When I first started in nursing, I really had no pointed intentions for my career future. However, I did know that one day, I'd need a master's degree. That's just the culture that's been created in healthcare and in nursing. So I started a Master's of Science in Nursing program while still working at the bedside. It was a busy time for me as a full-time employee and part-time student, but I was learning a lot. That's the great thing about graduate programs: you choose to be there and choose what you want to learn. Little did I know, though, that there would be an opportunity to mix my school world with my career world so quickly, so tragically.

During the fall of my first year, I was entrusted to the care of a little 4-year-old boy who, without getting too specific, got injured and needed to be on a ventilator for trouble breathing. He was at a neighbor's house with his parents and fell off his bike, hitting his head a little too hard. The hospital is very reputable for being a great trauma center and for providing intensive care treatments. The emergency responders were on the scene quickly and he came through the trauma bay even quicker. He was put on our trauma protocol and had been recovering very well up to this point. There was no reason for us to think that he wouldn't make a full recovery. At this juncture in his care, with what we've seen so far, any kind of morbidity or mortality was highly unlikely.

On the particular day I was taking care of this little guy, he was on day five in the ICU, and it was time for us to try taking out the endotracheal tube that was helping him breathe. He's already had his sedation medication taken down, and we had weaned the ventilator to settings that are acceptable for him to breathe on his own with some non-invasive support.

One of the best parts about bedside care is the ability to build a relationship out of thin air. You start out as complete strangers and all of the sudden trust, understanding, and respect appear. I felt pretty comfortable with this family right off the bat, and as we were chatting, I got to know them. They were nervous and because of this, in order to put their mind at ease, as I'm explaining the process of extubating (and I remember this like it was yesterday) I said,

"It'll be ok, we are going to be right here with you, and worst-case scenario, if he doesn't tolerate the tube being out we'll just put it right back in and he'll just need some extra time on the ventilator."

Well, we finished our discussion, the PICU doctors were finished with a.m. rounds, and we had everyone we needed at the bedside.

Three...two...one...deep breath, tube's out. One minute passes, he's struggling to breathe...a second minute passes, and his vital signs begin to fall. We didn't waste any more time, the code alert is called.

Just some insight on code team dynamics so you have a mental picture. If you've never seen a code team in action before it's quite a sight. It's teamwork at its finest in possibly the most stressful environment and most grim of situations. It's very bitter in its purpose but very sweet in its functionality. A Clinical Fellow usually is the team leader. There's two-to-three people interchanging doing chest compression; there's two-to-three people at the crash cart drawing up medications; and there are one-to-two people managing the airway depending on what's needed. In this case, there were two people trying to establish an airway. There's an RN documenting everything on a code sheet and thereby is instructing the timing of when things can be given, i.e. drugs. And there's another RN managing IV access and actually giving code medications. That was what I was doing in this case.

The code team arrives, people fill these roles, and we get to work. His O2 saturations continue to drop and soon after his heart rate falls to an alarming rate. We start doing chest compressions and start pushing code medications, such as epinephrine. All the while we're attempting to provide adequate air flow through bag/mask ventilation while trying to get the ET tube back in, but his airway had become so swollen from the extubation that we were having a really difficult time re-intubating. Ten minutes or so pass and we still don't have an airway established. He's in a full-on arrest. The 'critical airway' team is called and comes to the bedside. They are built of Anesthesia and ENT MDs. Airway experts. They continue with the airways while we carry on the code.

The timeline of this next phase is hazy but eventually the critical airway team reinserted the tube, and an airway was established. We spent the remainder of the time working on obtaining a pulse.

The entire code event lasted 32 minutes. It was a successful revival as we got the airway reestablished and got a pulse back, but it was a long code and he spent quite a bit of time without an adequate airway. He wasn't in good shape.

What happens to the parents during this whole thing?

Typically, when a code is called, a chaplain is part of the team. He/she takes the family out of the room and away from the situation. They are, rightfully so, hysterical in most cases and the chaplains do a great job of explaining what's happening. A couple minutes into this code that's exactly what happened.

The parents came back in around that 30-minute mark, very emotional. Stunned might be a better word. They were updated about the situation from the MDs, took in all the information, and weighed their options. Because of his clinical instability and the length of the code event, they decided to withdraw care. They were afraid, because of the duration of the event and the time he'd spent without good oxygenation, that their son had been neurologically lost. They thought that he wouldn't recover. That, coupled with the trauma they all had been through, they felt that withdrawing care was the best thing to do.

I am not even going to attempt to pretend that I know what it's like to make that sort of call. In fact I don't want to even attempt to imagine it, but that's what they had decided. Once these parents made the decision, they requested that everyone else leave the room except for myself. The team took him off of the ventilator, off the monitor, and disconnected from all IV medications. Given his situation, he's not able to withstand life without machine support so it was only a matter of time. He's handed to the parents to hold, finally leaving them with me in the room.

The dying picture and process is a struggle to watch, for multiple reasons. One of my jobs is to keep the boy comfortable with medication support as he's navigating through the process. That's exactly what I did.

Eventually time of death was called, and I'm left watching these parents say goodbye to their child. Watching them talk to their child for the last time. The only thing I can think about is looking them in the eyes hours earlier and saying,

"Worst-case scenario, we just put the tube back in..."

We went from extubating the patient after a life-altering event to the parent's completely saying goodbye. Safe to say everyone was devastated. There is no normal protocol for this type of situation. How could there be? Most of the time after a death the immediate family sticks around while the body is cleaned, extended family may or may not come, prayers are said, and then the body is put on a stretcher and taken downstairs to the morgue.

Grief-stricken and heartbroken, these parents decided they could not bear to stick around any longer. They say their final goodbyes, exchange information on what will be done with the remains, and leave. The transition of the body was then left up to me. I cleaned him up, took out all IVs/tubes that I was allowed to remove, said a prayer, and put him into a white zip-up shroud.

Eventually, security arrived with a stretcher, which I'd used before with other patients for transport. Not today though, it didn't feel right to me putting him in that thing, in that box. So I did something I'd never done before. I put a sheet over him and I carried him. I felt he deserved at least that. He deserved that final touch. It's a walk and a feeling that I'll ever forget. It's a boy I'll never forget.

Overall, a terrible story, but being in school had me connecting some dots from what I was learning in class to this unexpected, unfortunate event. I was taking the 'Information Systems in Healthcare' class and one of the things I was learning about was Lean, Six Sigma, and Quality Improvement methodology. That whole experience, in adjunct with this new knowledge, made me realize that there was opportunity here. It made me ask, how can we do things better? How can we improve our system? Unfortunately, things happen that are very difficult, if not impossible, to predict but that doesn't mean we can't try. We had a standard protocol for extubation preparation but it could be enhanced. It can vary from clinician to clinician. From the way a ventilator is weaned to the labs values they like to look at and deem acceptable to post-extubation practice. We could shed more light on those specifics.

A new improvement project was born. A team was developed and together we took a deeper dive into research, evidence-based practice, and current practice. Our collaboration created an extubation checklist that was comprised of all the necessary components to help ensure not only a successful extubation but also more specific mitigation in case of a failure. It also began a bunch of work looking into critical airway issues and how we approach them.

It's really hard to see learning from tragedy. Especially when there's no clear explanation and when it's so unexpected. The anger and grief can break you. You have to let yourself feel it but I've found that it's more constructive to channel it and redirect it towards something positive. Otherwise it consumes you. The work that stemmed from this relationship continues to grow even today. It changed the way I took care of future patients and ignited change across other clinicians as well as other disciplines to ensure it never happens again. I think about that day and that family almost daily. It's not something I've been able to forget but something that I've carried forward to things beyond the bedside. The bedside experience, as a whole, brought new levels of perspective to my personal life that I never would have anticipated.

Chapter 18

Be a Part of Something

A nurse's life is an intriguing one. It's not nine-to-five like most professions as the hours are strange. The majority clock in and clock out for three "12 hour" shifts per week, however, any nurse who has worked at the bedside knows that "12 hours" is an extraordinarily loose term. Most days, it's more like 13-14 hours because no one wants to pass off their patient to the next person with a list of unfinished work or incomplete documentation. So you stay until the work is done and then think about everything you may have forgotten on the way home.

Many outside the field have opinions about the three-day work week schedule, believing it is great to have four days off every week. It is, don't get me wrong. Having that many days off per week is great, but as with anything else there are risks and rewards.

The days worked are erratic, changing week to week; the days worked don't allow you to do anything else that day; the days worked leave you so physically and emotionally exhausted that all you want to do is go to bed or indulge with a glass of wine afterwards. Then there are the weekend, holiday, and night-shift rotations. They're required, necessary, and part of paying the dues. Communication with the outside world is minimal to non-existent while working, and during the winter months, its dark when arriving and dark while leaving. Lastly, permission and coverage to go to the bathroom, to take breaks, and to eat meals are part of the job.

While I didn't paint the prettiest picture, all that being said, there isn't a better way I could've spent the first six years of my career. All things considered, bedside nursing was the most exciting, rewarding, and humbling experience of my life. I developed closer relationships with the people I worked with and enjoyed the output of my effort more than anything I've ever done.

The connections developed with colleagues in a hospital setting bring a sense of belonging that's essential to doing this work. Those people were who I depended on when in the weeds, who I depended on when my patient was dying, who I depended on for emotional support when my patient passed, and who I'd laugh with when the toddler I was caring for peed all over me.

Love and belongingness needs are the third level of Maslow's Hierarchy of Needs. It resides after physiological and safety needs have been fulfilled, the third level of human needs is social and involves feelings of belongingness. The need for interpersonal relationships motivates behavior. Examples include friendship, intimacy, trust, and acceptance, receiving and giving affection and love. Affiliating, being part of a group (family, friends, work).

I can only speak for myself, but there's a reason I've found my way back to the ICU after years of exploring other arenas of the hospital. There's a sense of family and belonging that I've never experienced anywhere else except my own home. The friends I made and relationships I developed provided trust and acceptance. It makes me believe in how good people are and how good they want to be. My involvement within the hospital and the connections I've been able to create have taught me how to be a better man, and my experiences at the bedside, both tragic and otherwise, have given me a perspective that go well beyond a "career."

Part 3

BEYOND

Chapter 19

Give It Your ALL

The process of having a child is an experience unlike any other. I always knew I wanted to be a father and it was merely a matter of when, but I had little clue what to expect. When my wife, Kelly, became pregnant, we were in the right place in our lives. We had a stable home, good jobs, and were ready to take on the responsibility of parenthood. The pregnancy was uneventful (for me) and typical. She went full term (actually a week late), and didn't have any health issues. The delivery was also without complication and our first son, Fitz, was born a happy, healthy baby boy.

I had this expectation of becoming a dad that I would look into my son's eyes, he'd hold my finger, and we'd be immediately connected. It didn't happen like that for me. I immediately loved him but it came from an "I'm his father and am responsible for his well-being" place as opposed to a place of genuine connection. I knew in those first moments that I'd always be there for him, but I didn't feel that over-whelming connective love that you always read about or see in the movies. I also didn't cry. The love started out more primal for me. I was happy and excited but also felt ashamed that I didn't feel how everyone else I ever knew seemed to feel when their children were born.

Fitz was born at 5:36 p.m. on a Friday. When you have your first child, it's typically a two-night hospital stay. There are a lot of odds and ends to figure out before heading home and the hospital wants to make sure you're comfortable with the new addition to your family. We were taken to the postpartum unit shortly after the birth for recovery and were fortunate to have a great room with a view that overlooked the city. The first morning we were there, Kelly was still sleeping, and Fitz woke up. I decided to pick him up and sit in the rocking chair while looking out the window. It was right at sunrise. That was the moment I knew my connection with him was a growing process. Up until that point, I still felt like I should feel differently, like I was supposed to be consumed with these overwhelming feelings of heart-sobbing love. It was this moment though, during a phenomenal sunrise that I was sharing with my 12-hour-old son that grew our love. It was time stopping and unique; something that he won't remember but I'll enjoy telling him about for the rest of my life. It taught me something important as well.

It was like my connection with him had a barometer attached to it that had a baseline of one; one being my basic protective instincts over him and my fatherly love towards him. The early morning moment we were sharing together instantly moved my barometer up a notch. That's when I knew that our bond was something that would only continue to grow and not be something that I should expect to be instant or immediate and then plateau. It's an evolving, gradual climb that takes time. I would need to be there for him, always, and constantly put forth the necessary effort to communicate effectively with him. I knew how special he was from the very beginning and it didn't take long for that barometer to quickly move from fatherly instinct to pure unconditional love. That may not be the way it happens for everyone but that's the way it happened for me. That's parenthood.

Two years later our second son, Lincoln, was born. Having been through the experience already my expectations were set, from a connection standpoint, but this time we didn't find out the sex beforehand. That adds an entirely different element and I highly recommend it as the excitement builds to an entirely different level. That being stated, this kid threw us for multiple loops in the early goings of his life.

During his birth, I was at Kelly's right-hand side, trying to be as supportive as possible, when his head crowned through. Immediately I could see that the umbilical cord was wrapped around his neck. I looked at the doctor, who said:

"Oh boy...." (*Not* what you ever want to hear.)

The doctor quickly unwrapped the cord and a few seconds later Lincoln started crying. Those few seconds might as well of been an eternity, as all I could think of were the unfortunate things I'd seen in the PICU; all the tragic misfortunes and accidents that caused people to lose their children. Thankfully, that wasn't our experience and it made me extremely appreciative of his well-being. We were discharged the next day with a full bill of health across the board.

Lincoln struggled eating early on. It was as if he was trying to drink from a water hose and his upper GI tract just couldn't catch up with the supply. A few days after being discharged from the hospital, Kelly was feeding him around 11 p.m. I typically would go into his room while she breastfed, mostly just to give moral support. Well, he seemed to be having some difficulty so I held him for a bit to give a break when he suddenly appeared to stop breathing. His mouth opened and he seemed to be holding his breath; it'd last for a few seconds then he'd cry out. It happened again, he turned red, and then his lips started to look blue. Kelly put him on the changing table and I called 911. It was terrifying. He was having spells of 5–10 seconds of apnea (no breathing) before then crying out again while his lips continued to turn blue. The operator was great on the phone and talked through it with me.

During this time, Kelly was continually attempting to suction him with a bulb, eventually sucking out a plug in the back of his throat. This occurred right as the fire department knocked on our door. The paramedics came in and checked him out. Thankfully, he was calm and breathing well at this time as Kelly took care of it, but we also felt bad for making the first responders come to the scene. This being the second frightening event in almost as many days as he'd been alive, we were on pretty high alert.

Navigating life with two young children is no joke. Lincoln hasn't had any more episodes and is now a completely healthy little boy, but being a parent of two has tested everything I thought I knew about myself. There's no playbook and no one could've prepared me for the amount of patience and resilience I need on a daily basis. The amount of good moments far outweighs the difficult ones as they're the most fun, yet challenging, pieces of my life. It's an interesting dynamic because there's no place I'd rather be and it's a constant learning process. If effort and communication are key in my professional life, they've been doubly important in my personal life.

Take discipline for example. We don't believe in physical punishment and try to exemplify very little negative reinforcement. We more operate on the premise that every choice or action has an outcome associated with it, a consequence. Tasks can be completed the easy way or the hard way, and the boys can choose which method they'd like. If they're not listening, they have an opportunity to change that behavior; if not, then we do things in a way that, hopefully, they can learn from. If reactions to that are poor, then a consequence is in order. Usually it's in the form of timeouts, which can be very effective but have to be delivered firmly and with patience. When they get put in timeout they're not allowed to get up until they calm down and show a readiness to rejoin us. Before getting up, three things must happen: look in the eyes, tell why they're in timeout, and apologize if necessary. They have since come to view timeout as an unwanted consequence. There are days it takes a ton of effort to be patient with this process and days where giving a good spanking would probably be easier, but what does that teach?

I get to be with my sons every single day, and in that time I've come to value the little things. Reading, wrestling, walking, watching a movie, you name it; these activities are all part of our growing relationship, and they are important to me. I want my connection with my boys to be one of mutual respect and understanding. They'll know that they can trust me, talk to me, and that I'm their parent and their biggest supporter. It doesn't have to be one or the other, and in my opinion, it should be both. If I put forth the effort to communicate well in both roles I'll have a connection that far exceeds my original expectation.

Chapter 20

What Can Happen If You Don't...

I had never been a direct bedside provider and father at the same time. My days as a bedside nurse were spent single, as a boyfriend/ fiancé or husband, but never a father. I used to have families ask me if I had children, which I'd always answer 'no,' only to have them respond with:

"Well, you don't quite understand then."

I always scoffed at this a little bit (in my head), after all I had taken care of the sickest of the sick, seen plenty of death/dying, and changed uncountable amounts of diapers. None of that mattered though, because those parents were right. I didn't really understand the hardship of seeing my own child sitting there in bed, suffering, and me next to them unable to help. Powerless. On the flip side, all of that experience did help me transition into fatherhood and gave me a lot of perspective.

While directly working at the bedside I used to carry "the trauma pager." Patients brought into the emergency department via ambulance or helicopter were labeled as trauma, which usually meant they sustained an unexpected injury (e.g., gun shot, car accident, fall, etc.) that needed immediate treatment/intervention. Intensive care nurses were expected to respond to these events and provide assistance, mainly with drawing up medications or communicating with the unit when a transport decision is made. There's a lot of activity happening in the trauma bay when these patients arrive on the scene. The room is filled with emergency department doctors/nurses, ICU doctors/nurses, pharmacists, EMTs, chaplains, and patient care assistants all working hard to achieve a common goal. Everyone has a specific role and a job to perform, especially the chaplain who usually is the one assisting the patient guardians who are watching from the outside. Unfortunately, there are some cases where you're not really sure what to think when it comes to patient guardians.

It was always an unspoken assumption that when you carried the trauma pager and "2-year-old fall" came across that meant a non-accidental trauma, which could mean abuse. Choosing to work in pediatrics brings a certain of pluses and minuses. Children haven't done anything to put themselves in these positions. They haven't maltreated their body for years with poor dietary choices, smoking, drugs, or alcohol. They're not electively choosing to undergo risky surgeries or procedures and they're not neglecting their own health by putting themselves in a future debilitating situation. Every single child deserves the opportunity to have a happy and healthy life. A non-accidental trauma completely robs an otherwise healthy child of that opportunity.

Unfortunately, that kind of thing happens quite frequently. In the United States, more than four children die from child abuse and neglect on a daily basis. Over 70% of these children are below the age of three. Boys (48.5%) and girls (51.2%) become victims at nearly the same rate and 2.9 million cases of child abuse are reported every year in the United States. As someone taking care of that child while they're in the hospital, having to interact with the guardian can be a real challenge. It's another aspect that never becomes easy. I've had them ask me:

"Does this hospital do brain transplants? If not, can you tell me a hospital that does?"

Sometimes they ask that because they want to genuinely save their child while other times, I speculate, it's so whoever is responsible won't go to jail for murder. Either way, the answer to that question is always 'no,' and a tough 'no' as well.

Having children is difficult and there's no question about that. After I had my own children, I could actually empathize with the parents who had been sent over the edge and done the unthinkable. Stress level is high, maybe you're in a tough life spot for any number of reasons, and the baby or young child is crying uncontrollably or behaving in a more challenging than usual manner until the parent snaps. I can empathize but absolutely cannot condone. The lesson I learned from this and from being at the bedside all of those years might be the most important one I ever learned. When feeling completely stressed, overwhelmed, and not knowing what to do about a child who is currently in a challenging state:

> Put them in their crib, or someplace safe, and take a breather. Walk away for a moment, collect yourself, and take a break.

They won't go anywhere and will be safe in the crib for a few minutes while you regain composure.

I've done this a couple of times while sleep deprived, irritable, and alone with two kids under three years. That walk or quick separation has made all the difference at times, even if it's only a couple of minutes. I usually go back with a different mindset and am in a much more composed state.

This lesson was amplified recently, while at the hospital walking through the unit. The role I serve now within the hospital doesn't have me directly caring for patients anymore but I'm not far removed. My workspace is on the unit so I can still go into patient rooms and talk to them or the family on a regular basis, but I don't administer medications or take vital signs anymore. One day I was doing safety rounding and while strolling through one of the unit pods, I came across a little boy, alone and not moving, staring up at the ceiling. He looked so lonely and didn't seem awake, even though his eyes were open. I asked the nurse about his situation and she stated that he was a non-accidental trauma that came in a couple of days ago. The story was that he fell off the couch, which broke a rib, caused his brain to bleed, and his retinas to hemorrhage. Not likely.

Based on what they'd analyzed through numerous scans and tests, it was determined that he'd never be the same little boy again. I decided to go into the room and be with him for a bit. I talked to him, stroked his hair, and turned on some relaxing music for him to listen to. All the while he just stared up at the ceiling. At this time I could only think two things: he reminded me of my youngest son, and how incredibly unfair this was. He didn't even get a chance. Furthermore, he has siblings. Could this happen to them if whoever did this isn't apprehended? Luckily, the suspect in this case was arrested but I'm unsure what the outcome was. But now what happens to the other children? Overall it's a lose-lose type of situation.

The quick connection with that young boy was a difficult one that I can only hope was two-sided. I can only hope that little moment in time, in the midst of such tragedy, reached him at a more spiritual level. Maybe it was a brief moment of peace for him. Being a parent should be a privilege, not a burden. If there's a situation where stress levels are unbearably high and it doesn't seem like there's another way, have the self-awareness to recognize that and manage it. Immediately reacting can turn a stressful situation into a life-ruining tragedy. Sometimes all it takes is a quick break. Put them down. Walk away for a minute. Keep um' safe.

Chapter 21

Striving for Emotional Intelligence

There's a lot that goes into managing personal behavior. Narcissistic and egocentric tendencies plague most people in some way, and I'm no different. It's just a matter of where we are on the spectrum. Therefore, it's natural to think that most people have their own self-interest at heart when making most decisions or choices. Again though, it depends on where in the narcissism spectrum a person falls that will determine how much their behavior will affect their ability to connect with someone. This is why I think being an emotionally intelligent person, or at least someone who attempts to be emotionally intelligent, really becomes a factor.

Emotional Intelligence is the ability to recognize and understand emotions in yourself and others and the ability to use this awareness to manage your behavior and relationships. This has actually been studied somewhat over the past ten years. Emotional Intelligence is thought to be a member of the class of Broad Intelligences. The concept of broad intelligences emerges from a hierarchical view of intelligence often referred to as the Cattell-Horn-Carroll or "three-stratum model." In this model, general intelligence, or g, resides at the top of the hierarchy, and it's divided at the second stratum into a series of eight intelligences. It's based on factor-analytic explorations of how mental abilities correlate with one another.

Intelligences fall into subclasses. One may reflect basic functional capacities of the brain such as mental information retrieval and the scope of working memory. A second class, such as auditory intelligence, is distinguishable by the sensory system with which it is most closely associated.

Emotional Intelligence fits in here with cognitive and processing speed—how quickly you pick up on things and then process them. This is considered, also, to be a class that focuses on Hot Information Processing. Broad Intelligences can be measured as hot or cold. Cold intelligences are those that deal with relatively impersonal knowledge such as verbal-propositional intelligence, math abilities, and visual-spatial intelligence. We view hot intelligences as involving reasoning with information of significance to an individual, in essence, matters that can make our blood boil. The things that matter most to people: senses of social acceptance, identity coherence, and emotional wellbeing. Repeated failures to reason well in these areas lead to psychic pain that at intense levels is co-processed in the same brain centers that process physical pain.

By thinking clearly about feelings, personality, and social groups, however, people can better evaluate, cope with, and predict the consequences of their own actions, and the behavior of the individuals around them. It's difficult, but in my opinion as important to teach and coach on as anything else. This can be a learned skill that takes repetition. What does an emotionally intelligent person looks like? They perceive emotions accurately. They use emotions to accurately facilitate thoughts. They understand emotions and emotional meanings. They manage emotions in themselves and others.

Now, I'm not an expert but since I've been a student of this I've been actively trying to improve upon my emotional intelligence. Not long ago my wife and I were planning a trip with the children to the beach with some family. At the current time she had just finished a post-master's degree and started a new job. This job had her working three days a week but those days were always lumped together and usually about fourteen hours in duration. Consequently, she had no time to do anything else during those days. She worked Monday through Wednesday, off Thursday, and we planned on leaving midday Friday. I worked on Thursday and had this idea in my head that, because she was off all day, all tasks preparing for the trip would be completed by the time I got home. She'd be packed, the boys would be packed, the house would be straightened up, the car would have some things stowed away in it, maybe dinner would be cooked/ready, and generally everything would be orderly. I couldn't have been more wrong about my expectation. The house was a complete wreck, nothing had been packed, the boys were rowdy, and the car hadn't been touched. Dinner hadn't even been thought about.

The initial reaction, in my head, was frustration and annoyance. Our household homeostasis was completely off and I wanted answers. What had happened here? What had she been doing all day? My body was demanding a reaction based on the emotions I was experiencing and it wanted it now. Remember, we had a one-and three-year-old at the time and she had just logged about forty-five hours in the past three days. Initially, I had forgotten this. She needed a mental health day, as anyone would, to do some things she wanted to do before going out of town for a week. Completely understandable. At first I didn't see this; I could only see what my own self-interest wanted to see. What my own narcissism demanded to see.

Luckily, I didn't react. I let my body reach reason and remembered how the week had gone and kept my cool. After all, what was getting upset going to accomplish? Nothing, most of the time sweating the small stuff never does. It wasn't going to check anything off our list or get things done faster. If anything, it was going to slow down progress. I rolled up my sleeves and we got to work, together. Now, we did talk about it later calmly and collectively, but it was a much more constructive and useful conversation than what would've occurred earlier.

Five years ago, I would've let my emotions get the best of me and said some dumb things. Again, this takes practice and learning, mostly through failure. Earlier I mentioned general intelligence as a system of mental abilities. If we think about what defines us, innately, it mostly comes down to IQ (cold intelligence), personality, and EQ (hot intelligence). Now the great thing about EQ is that it's adaptable, it can change, as opposed to IQ and personality, which are way more fixed across a lifespan. The trick is knowing what skills to work on in order to improve EQ. Namely, there are four:

Self-awareness: the ability to accurately perceive our own emotions in the moment and understand our tendencies across situations.

Self-management: the ability to use that awareness of our emotions to stay flexible and direct our behavior positively. This means managing our emotional reactions in situations and people, which is really difficult because it completely goes against instant gratification. It means we put our momentary needs on hold to pursue larger more important goals.

Social Awareness: the ability to accurately pick up on emotions in other people and understand what is really going on with them. Perceiving what others are thinking and feeling.

Relationship Management: the ability to use awareness of our own emotions and those of others to manage interactions successfully. This taps into the abilities of the first three skills. It ensures clear communication and effective handling of conflict. It's the bond that's built with others over time, and it's the result of how we understand people, how we treat them, and the history we share.

Practicing these skills have become extremely important to me. It's allowed me to check my own behavior and be more receptive to the emotional needs of others. In turn, barriers break sooner and connection occurs quicker. Furthermore, it's made me more aware of my own deficiencies in being an effective listener. Listening, as opposed to just waiting for my own turn to speak, engages me more into the other person's story. I ask more insightful questions and really try to help. I'm not sure I would've done this otherwise. Overall, I think working on emotional intelligence has improved my professional and personal life; probably more so of the latter which ultimately is most important to me. There's still so much to learn and work on, thus is life.

Chapter 22

Covet Your Partner

After I graduated from college, I lived with my best friend for a few years instead of living at home. I just didn't have any interest in moving back in with my parents after being gone for four years. We had an absolute blast living together. One day we were at a local watering hole for a few beers and began talking about the future. We had both already begun our entry-level jobs (me at the hospital and him in the business world) and he was ensconced in an eight-year relationship with his high school sweetheart as well. The conversation started to gear toward my "single" status and any future possibilities related to the female persuasion. At that time, I decided to make the bold prediction that I'd end up marrying a nurse; the odds just seemed too favorable considering I worked with ninety-five percent women. He didn't see it, so we decided to make a bet: if I marry a nurse, he has to give a speech at my wedding in his underwear; if I don't, I have to walk down the aisle in my underwear. Bold.

Not too long after that, I was working a day shift on a reasonably slow day next to a girl I had known but not all that well. She had a pretty easy assignment as well so we spent the good part of that day chatting. Eight hours into the shift, I went to the bathroom and as I was walking out I crossed paths with that girl I had been chatting with.

"Oh, you're here today?" she asked.

"Kelly, I've literally been talking to you all day long." I replied.

She giggled, put her hand on her face in slight embarrassment, called herself an idiot, and walked past me. It was super cute.

We went on a date a couple of weeks later and have now been married since 2012. Yes, my best friend did, in fact, give a speech during our rehearsal dinner in his underwear. A man of his word.

Marriage is a journey. A journey that sees many different interchangeable phases that start and stop many times over. Sometimes it calls for romance, sometimes lust, sometimes friendship, sometimes emotional support, sometimes self-sacrifice. One phase may be short and another long, then it may flip flop. They're situational and require recognition. After a child is born, it calls for emotional support and friendship, but after a year with two kids, it calls for more romance. How we navigate those phases is dependent on the effort we put forth and how well we communicate. Those things are vital to our marital connection and the ways in which they are practiced don't have to be grandiose; just a priority.

Kelly is a nurse, but is also a nurse practitioner. She ultimately went back to school for her acute care certification so she could practice in the PICU. When she signed up, we knew it would be difficult, but we've always operated under the "it's always better to try" mentality. It was a year long and required her to do over five hundred clinical practice hours. This was on top of her full time job that, all together, essentially equates to about sixty hours a week. Consequently, the days she worked, she had little ability or time to help with the kids. This required me to do the majority in terms of day care drop off/ pick up, meals, baths, and bedtime routine, on top of my full time job. Needless to say, it was a very busy and stressful time.

A couple of months into the school program, we were in the thick of it. She was really putting in the work and subtracting hours off her total and I was doing my best to juggle my responsibilities as well. This particular week we had an upcoming trip for my cousin's wedding that I happened to be officiating and stress was redlining. Attempting to get everything squared away with work, both kids (one of whom was sick), and packing proved difficult. Not to mention my nervousness for the ceremony mounting on top of it all. I didn't say anything because she had a lot going on and really wanted to get these clinical days completed. Noticing all of this, though, Kelly came up to me midway through the week and said,

"Hey, I rearranged my clinical hours and days from this week to next week so I can help more."

I was incredibly grateful and the timing couldn't have been better. The week went so much more smoothly and her awareness of the situation made all the difference. Self-sacrifice for the greater good of the family is an important concept to grasp. I can't do whatever I want to all the time and neither can she. It's not about being right or proving anything— it's about being a good partner. Her emotional intelligence here was impressive.

What I know about being a good parent comes from my mom and dad, while just about everything I know about being a good partner I learned from my brother. He's one of the hardest working people I know and his family comes first. He operates on not being there just to help but having a shared responsibility on daily family maintenance. Because of that, for me, things like doing the laundry or the dishes, organizing the house, and taking care of the kids aren't any one person's duties but are our duties. It takes strong daily effort to stay on top of being an effective partner, and showing value through communication is a simple, little way to show appreciation. It's not always easy, but simple. One evening, Kelly came home from work as I was folding laundry. It was late and I'd already eaten dinner so she nuked some leftovers. After she had finished eating, she cleaned her plate and put it in the dishwasher. While doing so she said,

"Hey, thanks for always emptying the dishwasher so I don't have to. I really appreciate it."

That simple act of appreciation meant a lot to me. It wasn't anything incredible but it didn't have to be in order to enhance our bond. She's great at showing appreciation and I try to reciprocate that as well. She does all the cooking and deep cleaning in our house. After a meal or when I walk into a clean house, I really make an effort to thank her for putting the time in to do those things. Navigating a marriage is, like most things, a learning process. One that requires both people to make an effort on house duties, work, and parenting. One that requires communication, so say "thank you," "I love you," and compromise. Kelly brings out the best in me and we complement each other well. Being a partner is more than just being a husband or wife; it's a lifestyle choice. It's a daily commitment that requires constant attention and attempts at connection. My life doesn't work without her. She's my rock, the most generous person I know, the best mother and wife, and owns my heart in my most cherished personal connection.

Chapter 23

Slow Down

I usually wake up at 5:30 a.m. every morning. I get up, take a shower, and pick out whichever outfit looks the least wrinkled because I was too tired or lazy to iron clothes the night before. Then I put my eyes in (contacts) and go downstairs to eat breakfast, gather everything I need for work, and then brush my teeth. Waking the boys up comes next because Kelly has already been at work for an hour by this point. They get to watch a little TV with some breakfast before the chaos that is changing the clothes of two kids under five at 6:15 a.m. Sometimes there's kicking and screaming, sometimes there's cooperation, but there's almost always negotiation.

"Daddy, I'll go first but Lincoln has to put his shoes on and brush his teeth first."

That's on a good day.

A screeching "NOOOOO!!" is a different yet fun scenario that plays out sometimes as well.

The best is when we're all in the car, about to pull out, and someone has to go to the bathroom. Classic.

The plan is to be rolling down the driveway by 6:45 a.m. and then to work by 7:30 a.m. Sometimes I fit a workout in after drop off, depending on what the day looks like, and if not the morning, I'll fit one in after work. We live and die by routine. I'm regimented as hell and the boys thrive on it. Almost to a fault. We've gotten pretty good at it, though, and most days go without a hitch, but we have bumps along the road. It's all part of the parenting experience.

I rarely forget anything. In all the hustle and bustle, all the rushing around, all craziness of the daily grind, I've gotten pretty good at not forgetting anything. Wallet, keys, phone, lunch, jackets, nap stuff, badge, books, and bags...then the nationwide quarantine of 2020 hit.

We were bunkered up at the house for weeks. I rarely left, maybe an occasional run for supplies, and when I did I always forgot my wallet. Me, the guy who could get up, get myself and two kids ready for school and out the door before 7 a.m. and not forget anything, was now forgetting his wallet to run ONE errand. More than once I found myself at the store without any means to pay for anything. Back in the car and back home I went. The funny thing is that it didn't bother me one bit. Strange, huh?

Well, I wasn't in a rush anymore. I wasn't running my ass off going from one place to another, endlessly, and trying to be on time. What a weird and strange time we were in. Shelter in place mandates, toilet paper raids, empty restaurants, travel bans, business closures, economic decline, and a lot of sick people. There were also more active people outside than I'd ever seen before, unprecedented humanity and friendliness, extreme lows in air pollutants, and a spike in family quality time.

Family quality time. We were given a mandated opportunity to spend time together with little to no distractions and no timetables. It wasn't always easy and we definitely got stir crazy, but in a time where life moves at a thousand miles an hour we were given a gift to slow down...and I like speed. When I wasn't working from the home office our days were filled with board games, Hot Wheels racing, puddle splash contests in the rain, dinosaur hunting, crafts, and driveway picnics. There were a lot of creative things happening during this time.

I have a friend who's also a nurse and a father of three daughters. He took this opportunity to spark his children's imagination. Every single day he'd dress up as a different character and devise an activity or lesson for the girls. From a mad scientist doing experiments to a gym teacher running a workout to Bob Ross teaching an art class; all came with a costume, a personality, and fun. That type of innovation required effort and a commitment to communicate in an incredibly special way. That type of love strengthened a beautiful connection.

Slowing down isn't so bad. It was another opportunity to learn; it was another opportunity to reflect and prioritize. I was able to connect with my family in ways I hadn't before. I was able to have deeper conversations with Kelly, and we laughed—a lot. Did we have low moments and occasional family fights? Sure did, but the overall experience gave us so much more that couldn't be measured objectively.

So, is a true connection rare? The best answer I can provide is that it doesn't have to be. I've had the good fortune of connecting with men, women, children, strangers, and patients—all loved ones. In my opinion, it's not limited to anything in my professional or personal life and it can happen today, tomorrow, and all the tomorrows to come. Its only limitation is personal desire. We have to want connection with one another. I believe it's essential to breaking down walls, reducing barriers, eradicating misunderstanding, and eliminating hate. It brings additional perspective where none existed, teaches me things I didn't know about myself, and can shine light in dark places.

Life is hard and being human comes with a lot of challenges. There are going to be hardships and losses along the journey, but one thing I know is that the good things—those good things that make life so beautiful—always stem from connection.

Six Keys to Connection

1. Make an effort.

2. Look people in the eyes.

3. Really listen.

4. Slow down and pay attention.

5. Tell the truth.

6. Don't quit, make an extra effort, and smile!

Epilogue

My work now is completely based on quality improvement within the healthcare system. My technical title is Clinical Quality Specialist (CQS). We apply methodology such as the model for improvement and LEAN (a type of improvement science that focuses on eliminating waste). It's all aimed at reducing harm experienced by the patient in the hospital (outside of their current disease process). Things like catheter associated blood stream infections, catheter associated urinary tract infections, surgical site infections, and ventilator associated pneumonia, peripheral intravenous infiltrates, and venous thrombosis embolism.

Hospital acquired conditions (or infections), also called HAIs, are prevalent in healthcare but decreasing, largely due to quality improvement efforts. There were an estimated 687,000 HAIs in U.S. acute care hospitals in 2015. About 72,000 hospital patients with HAIs died during their hospitalizations. Each day, approximately one in thirty-one U.S. patients has at least one infection in association with his or her hospital care, underscoring the need for improvements in patient care practices in U.S. healthcare facilities. My responsibility as CQS is to apply quality improvement science to the pediatric healthcare setting in order to decrease these HAIs and reduce preventable harm to children.

I knew very little about quality improvement when I began in this role. My only exposure was the little bit I had learned about in school. The hospital I worked for put me through training on the model for quality improvement that took months to complete. I was able to use all of the essential QI tools and methodology on a personal project, which helped me understand how I could apply it to health care. The hope was that this knowledge, coupled with clinical experience, would put me in an advantageous position to really make an impact.

Quality improvement methodology isn't terribly difficult to understand. The concepts are pretty simple and straightforward. It's something that has been used in the financial, manufacturing, and business world for decades. In the last ten to fifteen years, Healthcare has been catching up. That's where the tricky part comes into play. If we're looking at this objectively, patients are the product within the healthcare system. However, unlike the manufacturing world, patients are not all the same and can't be fixed in an assembly line. Every person is multifaceted and completely different; therefore, standardization can prove to be difficult based on the multitude of complexities. Processes can be analyzed, mapped, leaned, and tailored for quality, but it can take a great deal of time and usually patience. Nonetheless, it can be done, and done well.

As I navigated this world, I found myself drawing on my experiences at the bedside. The difficulty wasn't in applying the QI methodology but rather in building will surrounding the idea of making changes and doing something a different way. Building trust and developing relationships with the people who were making those changes was key. Connection with teams, on my part, was the way to make progress and it took strong effort as well as effective communication. The connection-building concept that had been so evidently useful at the bedside was now becoming just as important away from the bedside.

For example, I spent a couple years initially working in the operative area. One day I received an email from one of the clinical managers I had been working with. She wanted to get a team together to look at the institution's central line dressing use. We comprised a team of clinical leaders and bedside staff from four different units, then started dissecting this possible issue. After further review it was clearly a problem. Therefore, we initiated a quality improvement project designed to minimize frequent or unplanned dressing changes for pediatric catheters. LEAN methodology was employed in order to decrease waste within the dressing inventory and maximize value.

Our team spent a lot of time talking to other bedside nurses and measuring our outcomes with patients. We collected and analyzed both qualitative and quantitative data to create an evidence-based dressing inventory list. We collected data before and after implementing the new inventory to ensure that the quality of care was maintained. Comparing the pre- and post-intervention periods, we saw significant reductions in infections, number of dressings used, and cost.

The success of this project completely hinged on the team. They liked the idea, wanted to do something meaningful, and didn't want to do something that wouldn't sustain success. This took an incredible amount of connection with the people actually doing the work on their units. They put forth the necessary amount of exertion it took to maintain positive energy around the project, and they communicated openly, as well as often. We shared the results of our testing as well as the evidence that backed our interventions. This helped explain the "why" which is essential to any improvement project.

Emotional intelligence, and being a student of that, really helps within the healthcare setting. I struggle every day but never give up on my behavioral awareness and how to manage it in a constructive way. I try to lose the idea of perfection as much as possible but it's difficult in today's world. The place I've always found the most value is in the people of my life. Developing positive relationships and keeping an open mind is applicable anywhere—whether it's in an office setting, a meeting room, or a patient's room. The need to positively connect is there. Eradicate any preconceived notions or judgments and start building lasting connections with those around you today.

Notes

[1] Benjamin Pageaux, "Perception of effort in Exercise Science: Definition, measurement and perspectives," *European Journal of Sports Science* 16, no. 8 (2016): 885-894.

[2] Bruno Paula, et al., "The psychobiological model: a new explanation to intensity regulation and (in) tolerance in endurance exercise," *Brazilian Journal of Physical Education and Sport* 27, no. 2 (2013): 333-340.

[3] Sally O'Hagan, et al., "What counts as effective communication in nursing? Evidence from nurse educators' and clinicians' feedback on nurse interactions with simulated patients," *Journal of Advanced Nursing* 70, no. 6 (2014): 1344-1355.

[4] "Number of Youth Suicide by Age Group," Lucile Packard Foundation for Children Health, accessed April 12, 2020, www.kidsdata.org.

[5] Seok-Ho Yoon, et al, "Inflammatory pseudotumor in the mediastinum: imaging with fluorodeoxyglucose PET/CT," *Korean Journal of Radiology* 14, no. 4 (2013): 673-676.

[6] "Idiopathic Scoliosis in Children and Adolescents," American Academy of Orthopedic Surgeons, March 2015, accessed April 10, 2020, http://orthoinfo.aaos.org/topic.cfm?topic=a00353 accessed April 10, 2020.

[7] Sam McLeod, "Maslow's Hierarchy of Needs," *SimplyPsychology,* March 20,2020, accessed April 10, 2020, https://www.simplypsychology.org/maslow.html.

[8] "11 Facts About Child Abuse," Safe Horizon, *DoSomething.org,* accessed April 10, 2020, https://www.dosomething.org/us/facts/11-facts-about-child-abuse.

[9] John D. Mayer, et al, "The ability model of emotional intelligence: Principles and updates." *Emotion Review* 8, no. 4 (2016): 1-11.

[10] Bradberry, T & Greaves, J, *Emotional Intelligence 2.0* (San Diego: TalentSmart, 2009).

[11] "Data Portal," Center for Disease Control and Prevention, accessed April 10, 2020, https://www.cdc.gov/hai/data/portal/index.html.

Made in United States
North Haven, CT
02 February 2022